Virginia
Standards of Learning Success

POWERED BY
GO Math!

INCLUDES

- Virginia Standards of Learning Lessons
- Lesson Practice/Homework with Spiral Review

Table of Contents

Name _____

Problem Solving • Equal Shares

Essential Question How can you solve problems using the strategy *make a model*?

Learning Objective You will use the strategy *make a model* using cubes to make equal shares.

 Unlock the Problem

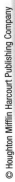

DIRECTIONS Make this cube train. Break it apart so two friends get equal shares. Draw the trains. Tell a friend about the trains.

Virginia SOL Success • 4.3a

one 1

Try Another Problem

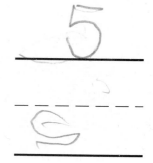

5

5

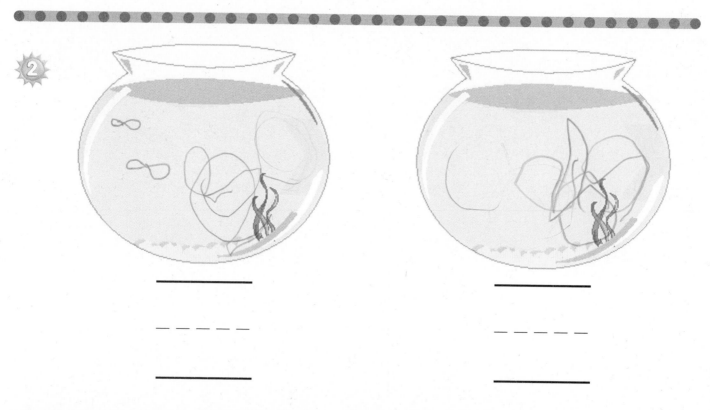

DIRECTIONS Maria wants to share the fish equally into 2 bowls. How many fish will be in each bowl? Use cubes to solve the problem. **I.** Place a cube on each fish as you count them. Write how many. **2.** Place an equal share of cubes in each bowl. Draw the cubes. Write how many.

2 two

Name _____

3

_____

- - - - - - - - - - -

_____

- - - - - - - - - - -

_____

4 ⊘

_____

- - - - - - - - - - -

_____

- - - - - - - - - - -

_____

DIRECTIONS Use cubes to model the problem. Draw and color the cubes. Write how many. **3.** Two friends share four beach chairs. How many chairs does each friend get? **4.** Two friends share eight beach balls. How many beach balls does each friend get?

Virginia SOL Success • 4.3a

Math Processes and Practices   MODEL • REASON • MAKE SENSE

On Your Own Real World

5

WRITE Math

_____

- - - - - - - - - -

_____

_____

- - - - - - - - - -

_____

6

_____

- - - - - - - - - -

_____

_____

- - - - - - - - - -

_____

DIRECTIONS Use cubes to model and then draw to solve each problem. **5.** Mom shares 6 water bottles equally in two coolers. How many water bottles are in each cooler? **6.** Grandma has more than 7 apples, but fewer than 9 apples. She packs an equal share of apples in two bags. How many apples does she put in each bag?

Problem Solving • Equal Shares

Learning Objective You will use the strategy *make a model* using cubes to make equal shares.

①

_____
- - - - - - -
_____
_____
- - - - - - -
_____

②

_____
- - - - - - -
_____
_____
- - - - - - -
_____

DIRECTIONS Use cubes to model. Draw and color the cubes. Write how many. **1.** Sofia put two shovels in two pails in equal shares. How many shovels are in each pail? **2.** Pedro put ten sand toys in two bags in equal shares. How many toys are in each bag?

Lesson Check

1

_____

- - - - - - - - - - -

_____

- - - - - - - - - - -

_____

· ·

2

_____

- - - - - - - - - - -

_____

- - - - - - - - - - -

_____

Spiral Review

3

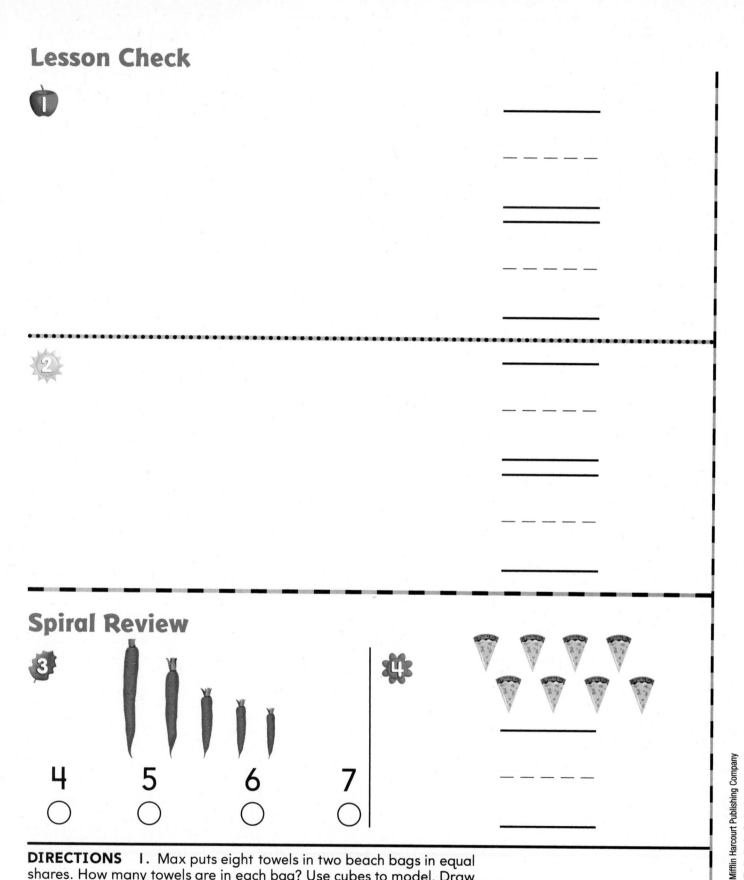

4   5   6   7
○   ○   ○   ○

4

_____

- - - - - - - - - - -

_____

DIRECTIONS   **1.** Max puts eight towels in two beach bags in equal shares. How many towels are in each bag? Use cubes to model. Draw and color the cubes. Write how many.   **2.** Ana puts four shells in two pails in equal shares. How many shells are in each pail? Use cubes to model. Draw and color the cubes. Write how many.   **3.** Count. Choose the correct number.   **4.** Count. Write how many.

6 six

Name _____

Count Backward from 10

Essential Question How can you count
and order numbers backward from 10?

Learning Objective You will
count backward by ones when
given any number between
1 and 10.

 Listen and Draw Real World

10	9	8	7	6	5	4	3	2	1	0

10		8		6	5	4		2	1	0

9   *7*   *3*

DIRECTIONS Point to the numbers on the top number path as you
count backward from 10. Point to the numbers on the bottom number
path and trace the unknown numbers as you count backward from 10.

Virginia SOL Success • 4.4a

seven **7**

© Houghton Mifflin Harcourt Publishing Company • Image Credits: ©Corbis Premium RF/Alamy

Share and Show

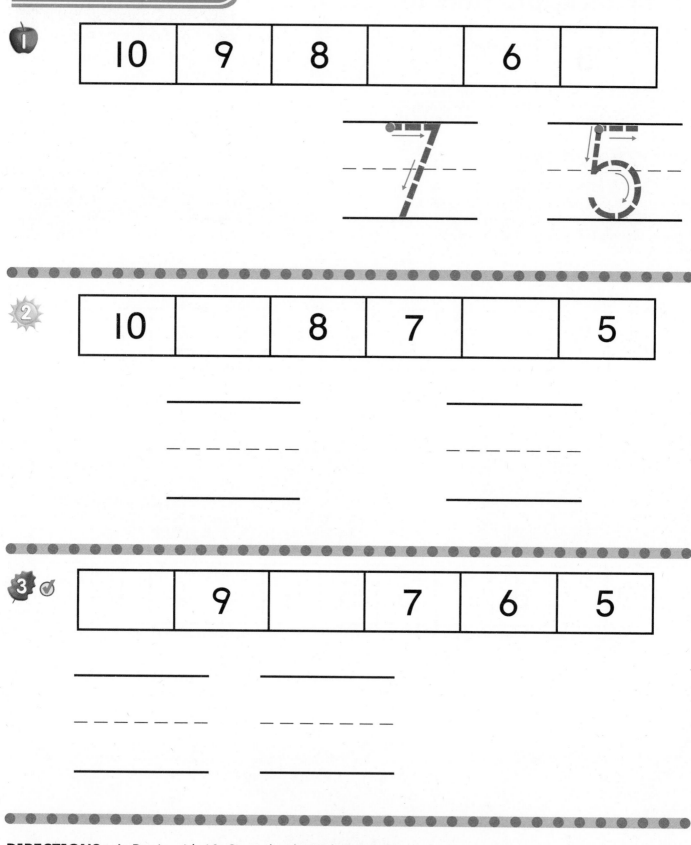

1

| 10 | 9 | 8 | | 6 | |

2

| 10 | | 8 | 7 | | 5 |

_____   _____

- - - - - - -   - - - - - - -

_____   _____

3 ✓

| | 9 | | 7 | 6 | 5 |

_____   _____

- - - - - - -   - - - - - - -

_____   _____

DIRECTIONS 1. Begin with 10. Count backward. Trace the numbers. **2–3.** Begin with 10. Count backward. Write the unknown numbers.

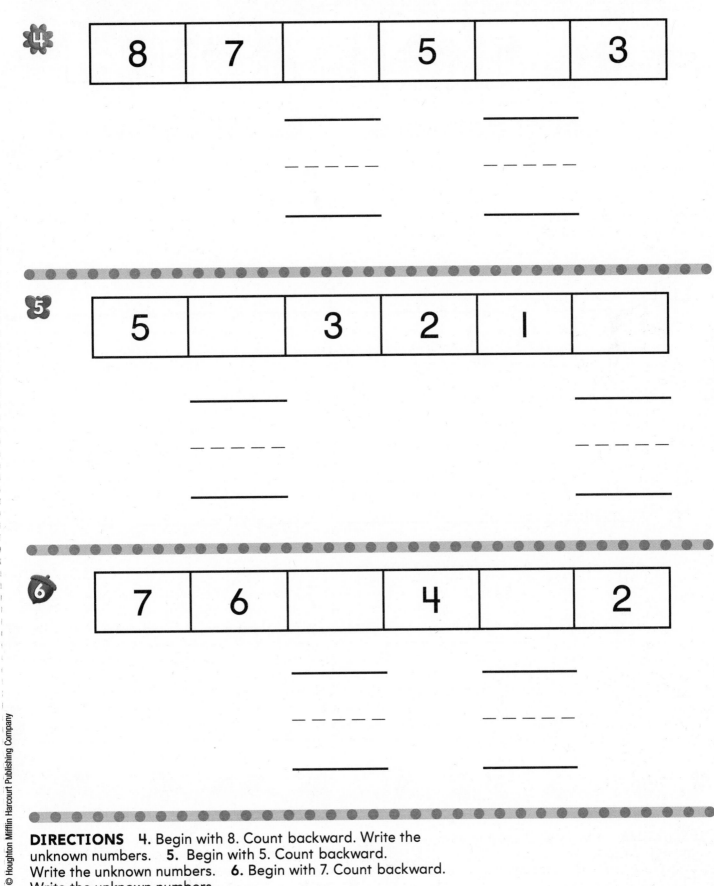

4 | 8 | 7 | | 5 | | 3 |

_____   _____

- - - - -   - - - - -

_____   _____

5 | 5 | | 3 | 2 | 1 | |

_____   _____

- - - - -   - - - - -

_____   _____

6 | 7 | 6 | | 4 | | 2 |

_____   _____

- - - - -   - - - - -

_____   _____

DIRECTIONS 4. Begin with 8. Count backward. Write the unknown numbers. 5. Begin with 5. Count backward. Write the unknown numbers. 6. Begin with 7. Count backward. Write the unknown numbers.

Virginia SOL Success • 4.4a

Problem Solving • Applications Real World

WRITE Math

	Count Forward	Count Backward
7 3 5 4		
8 7 8 9		
9 6 5 7		

DIRECTIONS 7–9. Look at the numbers on the left. Write the numbers in order counting forward. Now write the numbers in order counting backward.

HOME ACTIVITY • Write the numbers 0–10 on separate self-stick notes or on slips of paper. Have your child place the numbers in order counting backward from 10 to 0.

10 ten

Count Backward from 10

Learning Objective You will count backward by ones when given any number between 1 and 10.

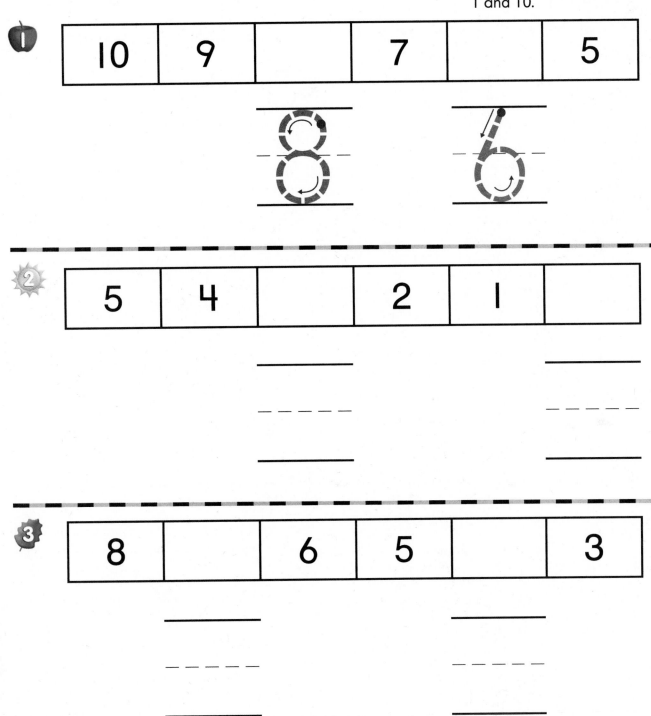

①

| 10 | 9 | | 7 | | 5 |

②

| 5 | 4 | | 2 | 1 | |

③

| 8 | | | 6 | 5 | | 3 |

DIRECTIONS 1. Begin with 10. Count backward. Trace the unknown numbers. 2 Begin with 5. Count backward. Write the unknown numbers. 3 Begin with 8. Count backward. Write the unknown numbers.

Virginia SOL Success • 4.4a

eleven 11

Lesson Check

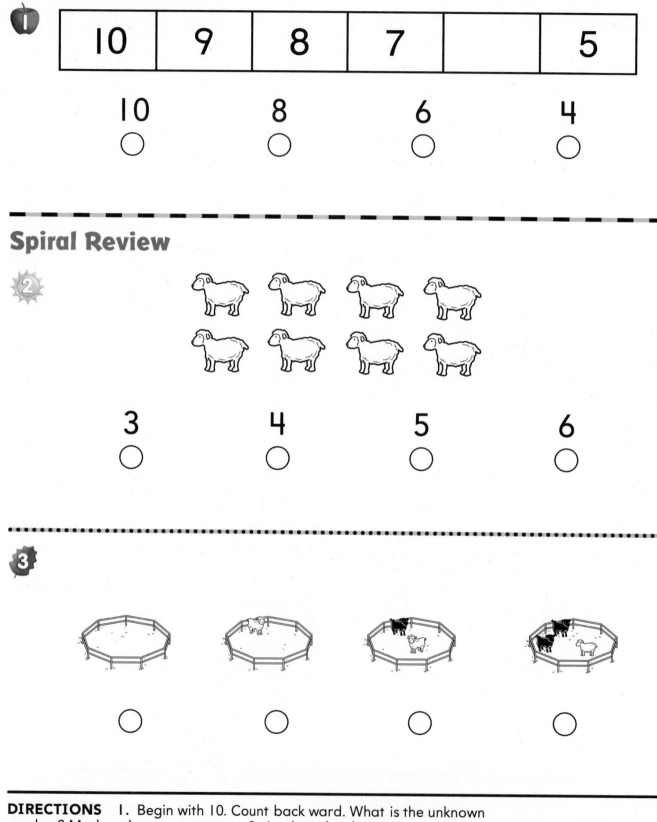

1

| 10 | 9 | 8 | 7 | | 5 |

10   8   6   4
○   ○   ○   ○

Spiral Review

2

3   4   5   6
○   ○   ○   ○

3

○   ○   ○   ○

DIRECTIONS 1. Begin with 10. Count back ward. What is the unknown number? Mark under your answer. 2. Look at the sheep. How many sheep would be in each share if there are two equal shares? Mark under your answer. 3. Which pen has 0 sheep in it? Mark under your answer.

12 twelve

Name _____

Compare and Order Sets from Greatest to Least

Essential Question How can you compare and order sets of objects from greatest to least?

Learning Objective You will compare and order 10 or fewer objects, from greatest to least.

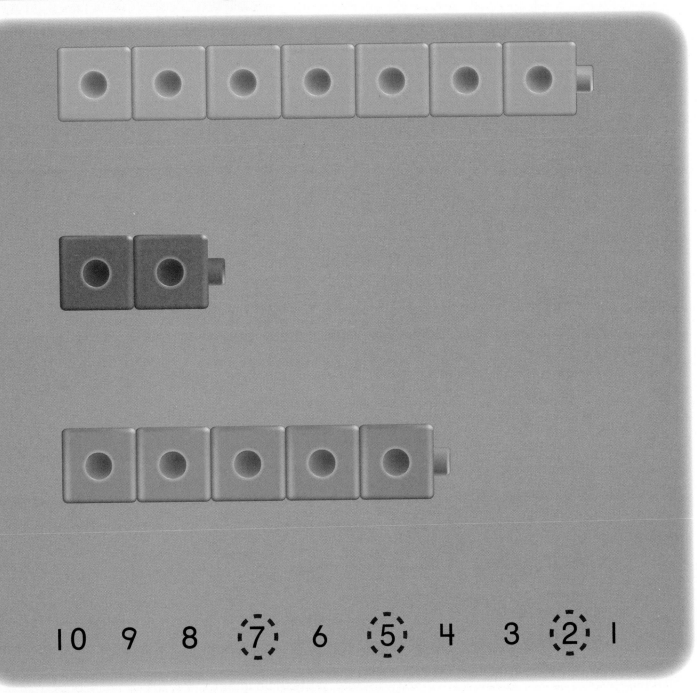

10   9   8   (7)   6   (5)   4   3   (2)   1

DIRECTIONS Count how many cubes in each cube train. Compare the cube trains. Trace the circle around the numbers for the cube trains in order from greatest to least.

Virginia SOL Success • 4.6a

thirteen 13

Share and Show

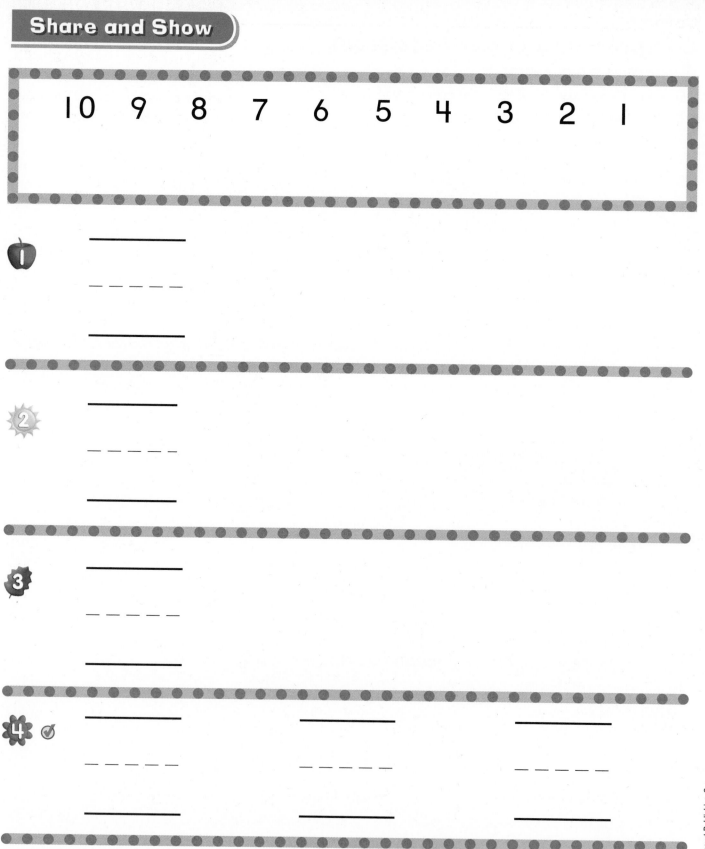

10   9   8   7   6   5   4   3   2   1

1.

2.

3.

4. ✓

DIRECTIONS 1. Place 8 counters in the workspace. Write the number. Draw the counters beside the number. **2.** Place 3 counters in the workspace. Write the number. Draw the counters beside the number. **3.** Place 6 counters in the workspace. Write the number. Draw the counters beside the number. **4.** Compare the counters you drew. Write the numbers in order from greatest to least.

14 fourteen

5 _____

- - - - - - -

_____

6 _____

- - - - - - -

_____

7 _____

- - - - - - -

_____

8 _____   _____   _____

- - - - - - -   - - - - - - -   - - - - - - -

_____   _____   _____

DIRECTIONS   **5.** Place 1 counter in the workspace. Write the number. Draw the counter beside the number.   **6.** Place 10 counters in the workspace. Write the number. Draw the counters beside the number.   **7.** Place 4 counters in the workspace. Write the number. Draw the counters beside the number. **8.** Compare the counters you drew. Write the numbers in order from greatest to least.

Virginia SOL Success • 4.6a   fifteen   **15**

Problem Solving • Applications

9

DIRECTIONS **9.** Makenna has 5 hats. One of her friends has more hats than her. Another friend has fewer hats than Makenna. Draw the hats. Write how many. Compare the hats. Write the numbers in order from greatest to least.

HOME ACTIVITY • Show your child three sets of 10 or fewer household objects. Ask him or her to count the number of objects in each set. Then have your child compare and order the sets from greatest to least.

16 sixteen

Name _____

Compare and Order Sets from Greatest to Least

Learning Objective You will compare and order 10 or fewer objects, from greatest to least.

1 _____

    - - - - -

_____

2 _____

    - - - - -

_____

3 _____

    - - - - -

_____

4 _____   _____   _____

   - - - - -   - - - - -   - - - - -

_____   _____   _____

DIRECTIONS 1. Place 6 counters in the workspace. Write the number. Draw the counters beside the number. 2. Place 3 counters in the workspace. Write the number. Draw the counters beside the number. 3. Place 9 counters in the workspace. Write the number. Draw the counters beside the number. 4. Compare the counters you drew. Write the numbers in order from greatest to least.

Virginia SOL Success • 4.6a

Lesson Check

_____

_ _ _ _ _ _ _ _ _

_____

_ _ _ _ _ _ _ _ _

_____

_ _ _ _ _ _ _ _ _

_____

_____   _____   _____

_ _ _ _   _ _ _ _   _ _ _ _

_____   _____   _____

Spiral Review

②

_____

_ _ _ _ _ _ _ _ _

_____

DIRECTIONS 1. Count how many cubes in each cube train. Write the number. Compare the cube trains. Write the numbers in order from greatest to least. **2.** How many birds are there? Write the number.

18 eighteen

Identify Plane Shapes in Different Positions

Essential Question How can you describe the location of plane shapes in different positions?

Learning Objective You will describe the location of plane shapes in different positions.

Listen and Draw Real World

DIRECTIONS Use blue to color the triangles, red to color the squares, and orange to color the rectangles.

Virginia SOL Success • 9.10a

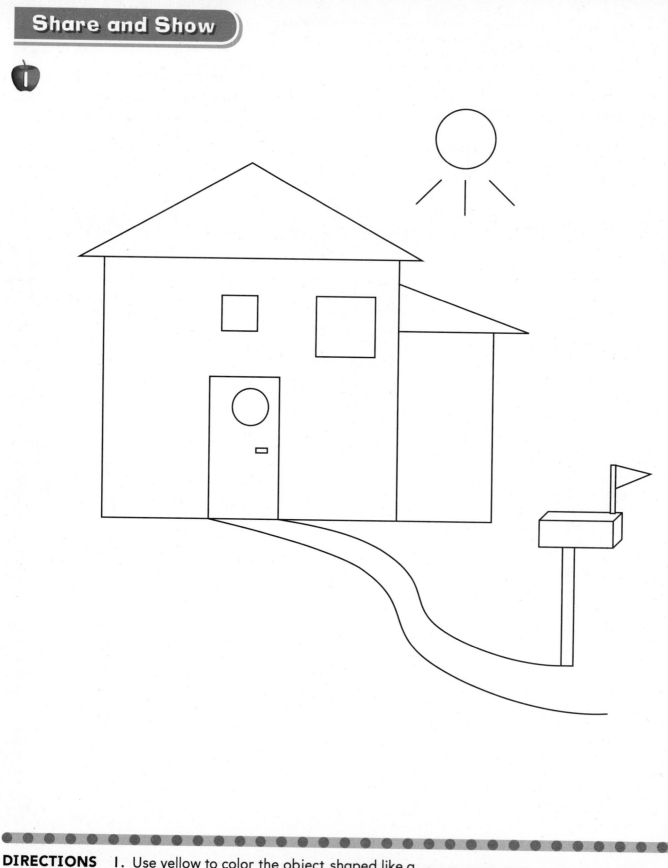

DIRECTIONS 1. Use yellow to color the object shaped like a circle that is above the object shaped like a triangle. Use blue to color the object shaped like a triangle above the object shaped like a square. Use green to color the object shaped like a square above the object shaped like a rectangle.

DIRECTIONS 2. Mark an X on the object shaped like a circle above the object shaped like a rectangle. Circle the object shaped like a square next to the object shaped like a circle. Draw a line under the object shaped like a triangle below the object shaped like a square.

Problem Solving • Applications Real World

DIRECTIONS   3. Draw objects shaped like a circle, triangle, square, and rectangle in different positions. Tell a friend about the position of the objects using the words *above*, *below*, and *next to*.

Identify Plane Shapes in Different Positions

Learning Objective You will describe the location of plane shapes in different positions.

DIRECTIONS Use blue to color the object shaped like a triangle below the object shaped like a circle. Use red to color the object shaped like a square next to the object shaped like a circle. Use green to color the object shaped like a triangle above the object shaped like a rectangle.

Lesson Check

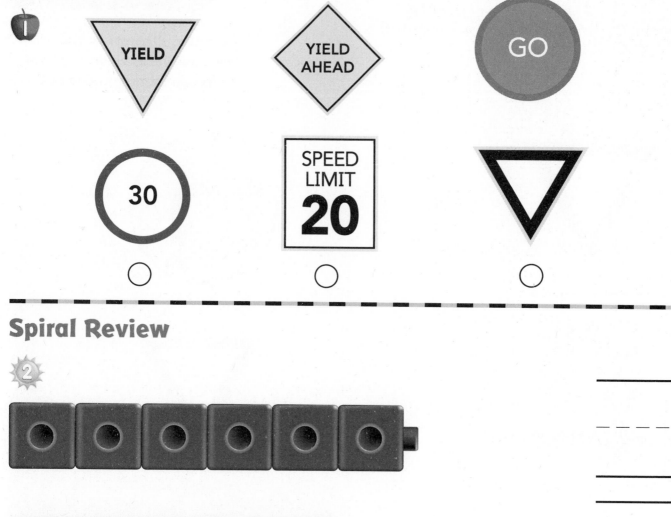

①
YIELD

YIELD AHEAD

GO

30

SPEED LIMIT 20

○   ○   ○

- -

Spiral Review

②
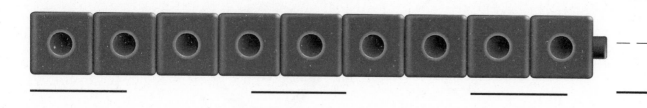

_____
— — — — — —
_____
_____
— — — — — —
_____

DIRECTIONS 1. Which set of objects shows an object shaped like a circle above an object shaped like a triangle? Mark under your answer. 2. Count how many cubes in each cube train. Write the number. Compare the cube trains. Write the numbers in order from greatest to least.

24 twenty-four

Name _____

Compare Volumes

Essential Question How can you compare the volumes of two containers to see which holds more?

Learning Objective You will compare the volumes of two containers to see which holds more.

DIRECTIONS Olivia has a dropper and a cup. She wants to find other containers that hold about the same amount as these objects. Trace the containers she might find.

Virginia SOL Success • 11.5a

Share and Show

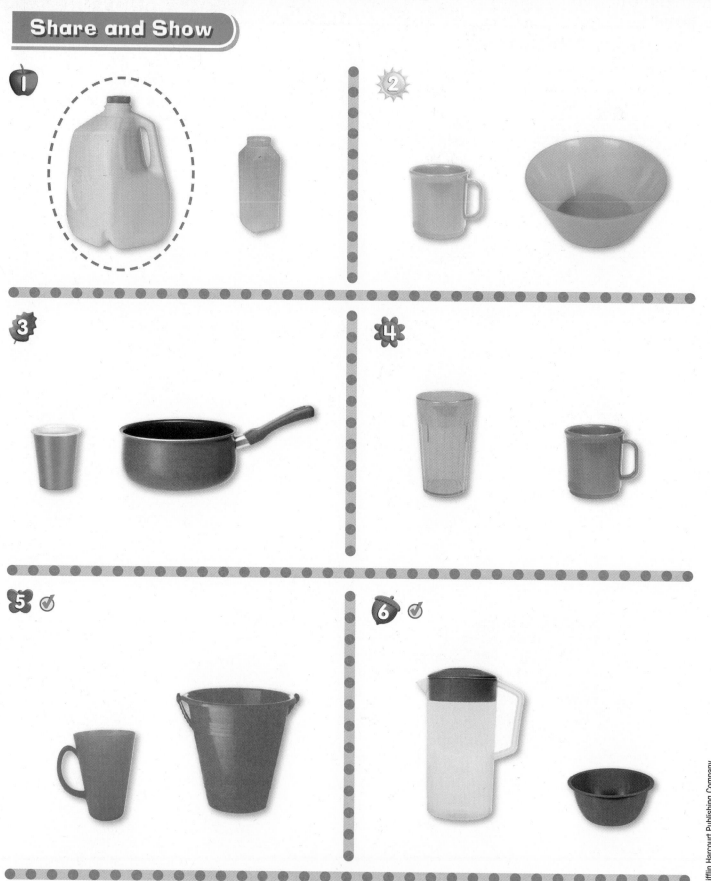

1

2

3

4

5 ✓

6 ✓

DIRECTIONS Fill one container with beans or rice. Pour it into the other container. **1.** Trace the circle to show the container that holds more. **2–4.** Circle the container that holds more. **5–6.** Mark an X on the container that holds less.

26 twenty-six

Name _____

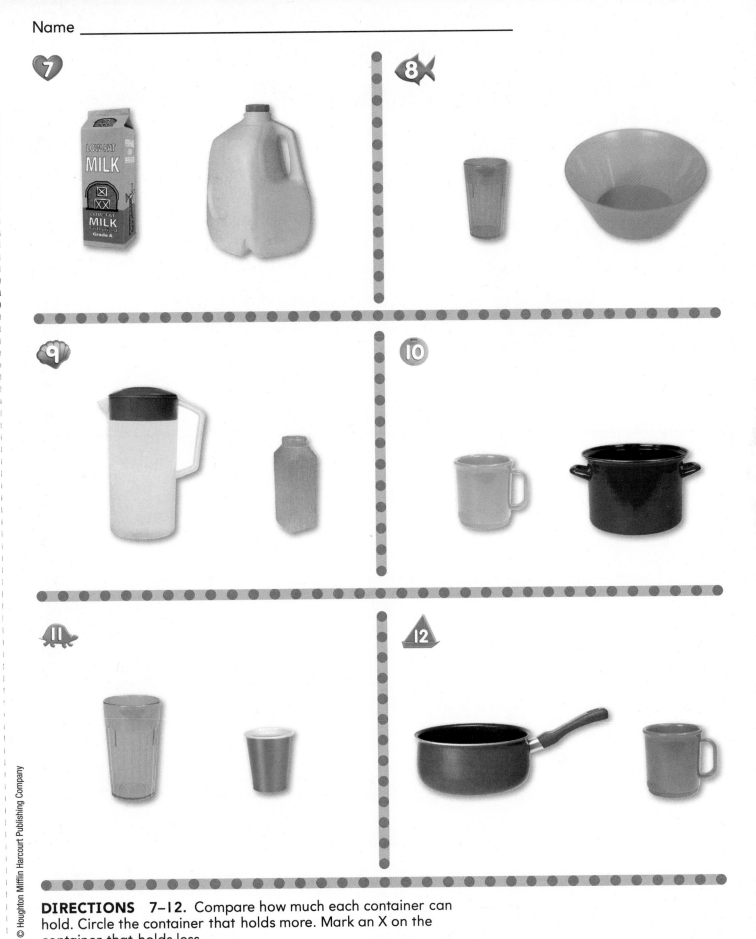

7

8

9

10

11

12

DIRECTIONS 7–12. Compare how much each container can
hold. Circle the container that holds more. Mark an X on the
container that holds less.

Virginia SOL Success • 11.5a

twenty-seven **27**

© Houghton Mifflin Harcourt Publishing Company

Problem Solving • Applications *Real World*

WRITE
Math

⭐ 13

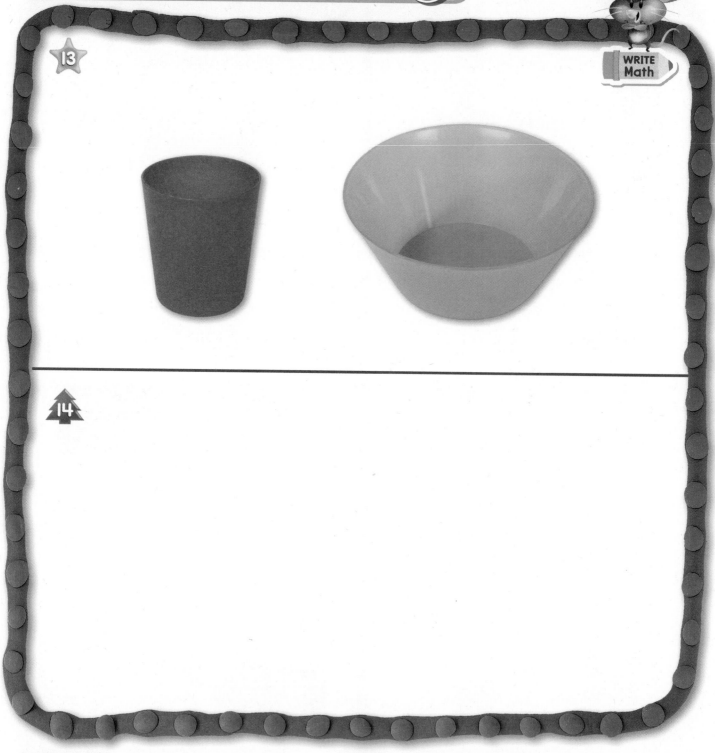

🎄 14

DIRECTIONS **13.** Petra pours a full blue cup of beans into the green bowl. The green bowl is not full. Mark an X on the container that holds less. **14.** Lucas used beans to fill a glass and a bowl. The bowl held more beans. Draw to show what the glass and the bowl might look like.

HOME ACTIVITY • Provide two different-sized containers. Ask your child which holds more and which holds less. Then ask your child how he or she can find out if his or her answer is correct.

28 twenty-eight

Name _____

Compare Volumes

Learning Objective You will compare the volumes of two containers to see which holds more.

DIRECTIONS Compare the volumes of each container. **1.** Trace the circle around the container that holds more. Trace the X on the container that holds less. **2–6.** Circle the container that holds more. Mark an X on the container that holds less.

Lesson Check

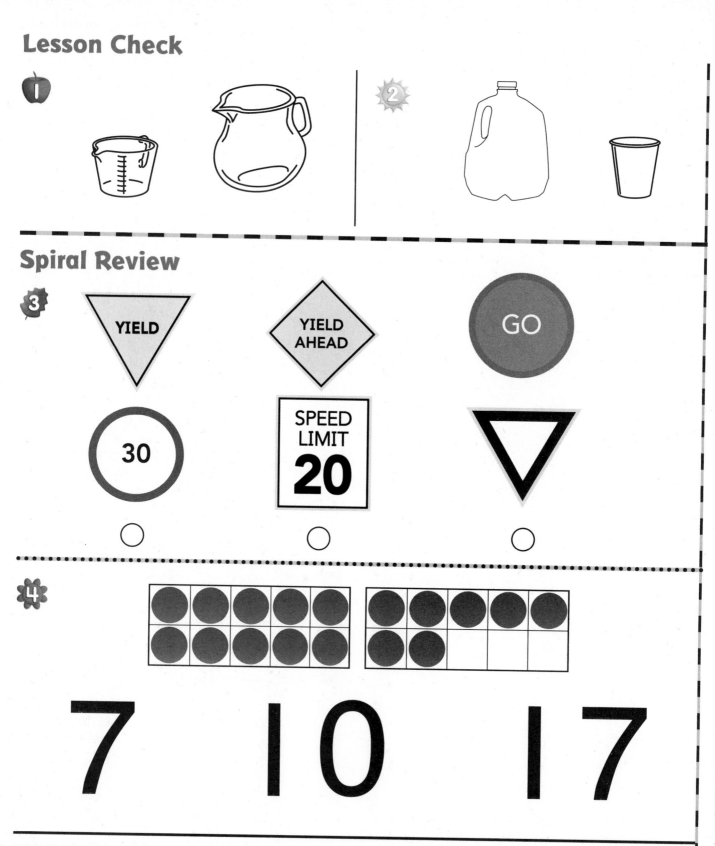

1

2

Spiral Review

3

YIELD

YIELD AHEAD

GO

30

SPEED LIMIT **20**

○   ○   ○

4

7   10   17

DIRECTIONS 1–2. Compare the volumes of each container. Circle the container that holds more. Mark an X on the container that holds less. **3.** Which set of objects shows an object shaped like a rectangle below an object shaped like a square? Mark under your answer. **4.** How many counters? Circle the number.

30 thirty

Name _____

Compare Temperatures

Essential Question How can you compare the temperatures of warm and cool objects and environments?

Learning Objective You will compare the temperatures of warm and cool objects and environments.

DIRECTIONS Look at the pictures. Trace the circle around the picture that shows a warm temperature. Trace the X on the picture that shows a cool temperature.

Virginia SOL Success • 11.5b

thirty-one 31

DIRECTIONS 1. Trace the circle around the picture that shows a warmer temperature than the first picture in the row. **2–3.** Circle the picture that shows something warmer than the first picture in the row.

Name _____

DIRECTIONS **4–9.** Look at each picture. Circle the picture in red if it most likely shows a warm temperature. Circle the picture in blue if it most likely shows a cool temperature. Tell a friend how you know.

Virginia SOL Success • 11.5b

thirty-three **33**

Problem Solving • Applications Real World

10

WRITE Math

11

DIRECTIONS 10. Draw to show an object you may use in a cool temperature. 11. Draw to show an object you may use in a warm temperature.

HOME ACTIVITY • Ask your child to name a favorite object he or she may use in a warm temperature. Then ask for a favorite object he or she may use in a cool temperature.

Name _____

Compare Temperatures

Learning Objective You will compare the temperatures of warm and cool objects and environments.

DIRECTIONS 1–2. Use blue to color the cool objects. Use red to color the warm objects. 3–4. Look at the picture. Color the clothing that you would most likely wear to play if you were there. Tell how you know.

Virginia SOL Success • 11.5b

Lesson Check

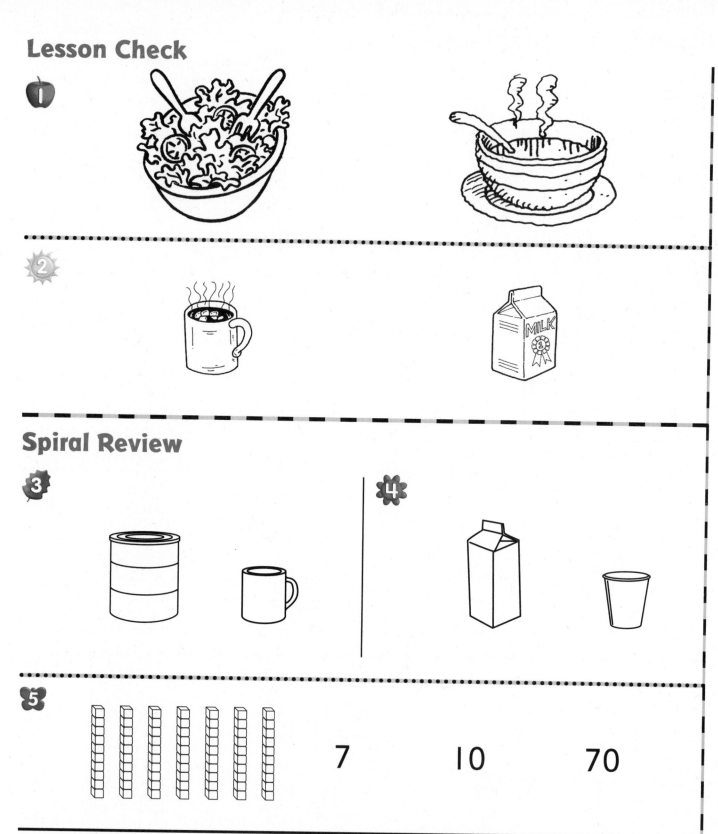

Spiral Review

7   10   70

DIRECTIONS 1–2. Use red to color the warm object. Use blue to color the cool object. 3–4. Compare the volumes of each container. Circle the container that holds more. Mark an X on the container that holds less. 5. Count by tens. Circle how many cubes there are.

Name _____

More Time, Less Time

Essential Question How can you compare the amount of time spent on two events as longer or shorter?

Learning Objective You will compare the amount of time spent on two events as longer or shorter.

DIRECTIONS Look at the pictures. Talk about whether it would take more time or less time to squeeze orange juice than to pour it from the carton. Trace the circle to show the activity that would usually take more time.

Virginia SOL Success • 11.5c

thirty-seven **37**

DIRECTIONS 1. Trace the circle to show the activity that would usually take more time. **2–4.** Circle the activity that would usually take more time.

Name _____

DIRECTIONS 5–8. Circle the activity that would usually take less time.

Virginia SOL Success • 11.5c

thirty-nine 39

Problem Solving • Applications

DIRECTIONS Draw two pictures to show what you know about activities that would usually take more time and less time.

HOME ACTIVITY • Ask your child which of two chores, such as making the bed and setting the table, would take more time. Have your child do both chores while you time them, and then compare which chore actually took more time.

40 forty

Name _____

More Time, Less Time

Learning Objective You will compare the amount of time spent on two events as longer or shorter.

1

2

3

4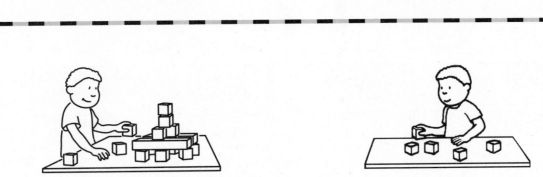

DIRECTIONS **1.** Trace the circle to show the activity that would usually take less time. **2.** Circle the activity that would usually take less time. **3–4.** Circle the activity that would usually take more time.

Lesson Check

1

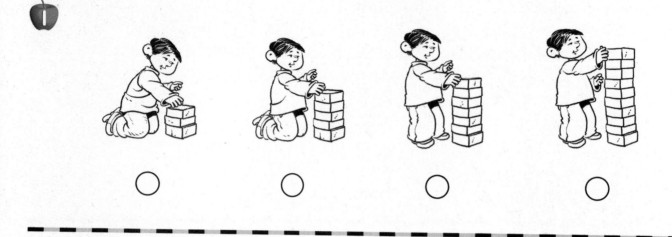

○   ○   ○   ○

Spiral Review

2

○   ○   ○   ○

3

17

○   ○   ○   ○

DIRECTIONS 1. Which tower took more time to build? Mark under your answer.   2. Look at the objects. Mark under the objects that are warm.
3. Which ten frames show 17? Mark under your answer.

Name _____

Days in a Week

Essential Question How can you understand time such as the days in a week?

Learning Objective You will understand time such as the days in a week.

Listen and Draw Real World

Sunday Monday Tuesday Wednesday Thursday Friday Saturday

DIRECTIONS Point to each day name as you say them in order. Circle the name for today. Draw something you would like to do today.

Virginia SOL Success • 11.5d

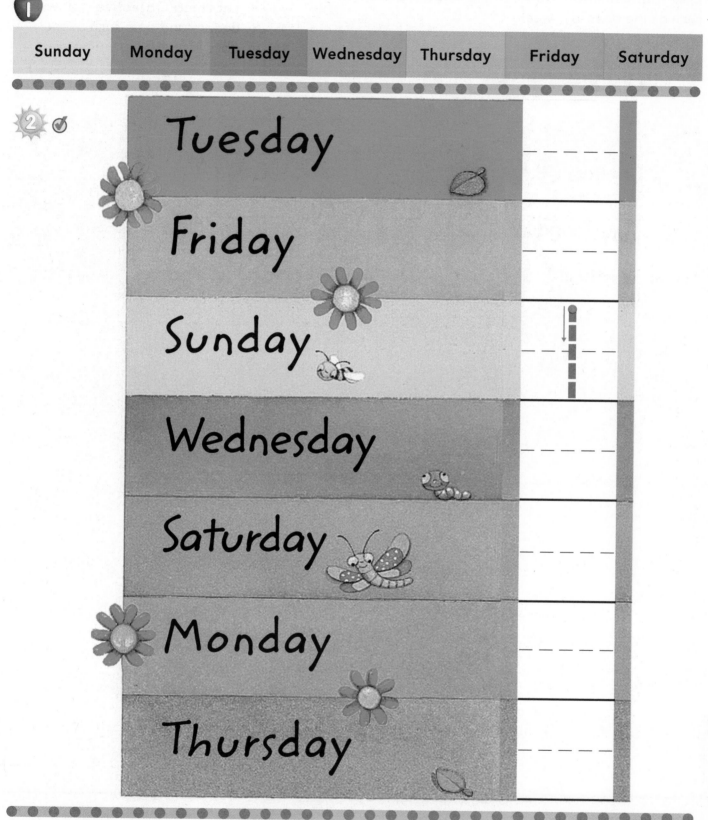

| Sunday | Monday | Tuesday | Wednesday | Thursday | Friday | Saturday |

Tuesday

Friday

Sunday

Wednesday

Saturday

Monday

Thursday

DIRECTIONS 1. Point to and say each day of the week. Circle the name for today. 2. Number the days in order beginning with Sunday.

44 forty-four

Name _____

Sunday

Monday

Tuesday

Wednesday

Thursday

Friday

Saturday

yesterday

today

tomorrow

DIRECTIONS **3.** Find the name of the day it is today. Trace the name. Draw a line to the word *today*. Do the same for the name of the day before today and the word *yesterday*. Do the same for the name of the day after today and the word *tomorrow*.

Virginia SOL Success • 11.5d

Problem Solving • Applications Real World

WRITE Math

6

5   6   7   days in a week

7

Monday   Wednesday   Friday

8

Thursday   Saturday   Tuesday

DIRECTIONS Circle your answer.
6. How many days are in a week?
7. Which day is two days after Wednesday?
8. Which day is one week from Saturday?

HOME ACTIVITY • Have your child say the days of the week in order beginning with Sunday.

Days in a Week

Learning Objective You will understand time such as the days in a week.

Sunday	Monday	Tuesday	Wednesday	Thursday	Friday	Saturday

1   **1**   **2**   **3**

2   basketball   art class   soccer

3   Monday   Tuesday   Wednesday

DIRECTIONS Circle your answer. **1.** On how many days is there an art class? **2.** What happens on Sunday? **3.** On which day is the violin lesson?

Lesson Check

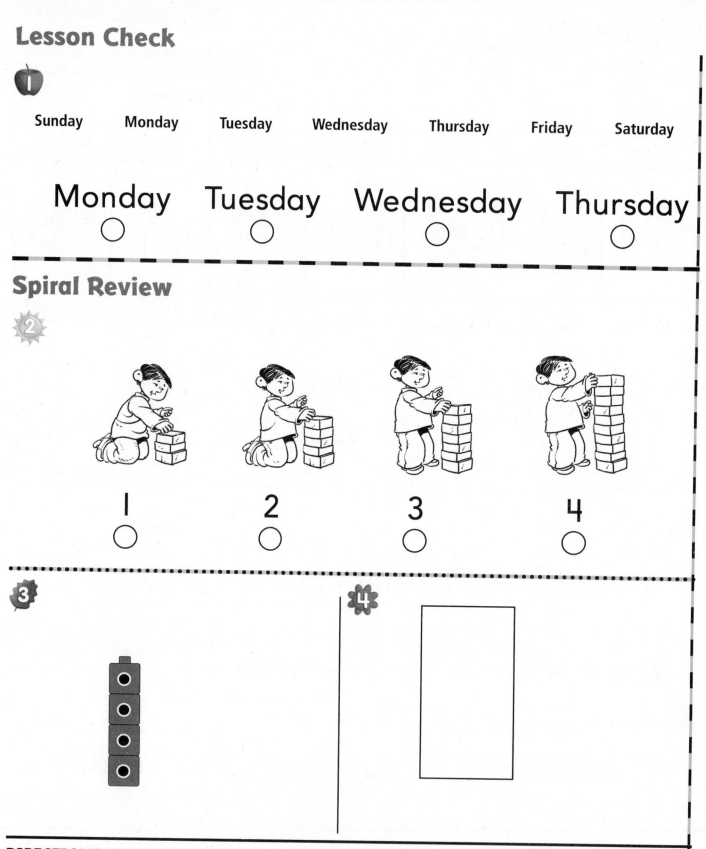

1

| Sunday | Monday | Tuesday | Wednesday | Thursday | Friday | Saturday |

Monday ○   Tuesday ○   Wednesday ○   Thursday ○

Spiral Review

2

1 ○   2 ○   3 ○   4 ○

3

4

DIRECTIONS **I.** Which day is three days after Monday? Mark under your answer. **2.** Which tower took the least time to build? Mark under your answer. **3.** Look at the cube train. Draw a train that is taller than this one. **4.** Draw a circle next to the rectangle.

48 forty-eight

Name _____

Weeks in a Month

Essential Question How can you understand time such as the weeks in a month?

Learning Objective You will understand time such as the weeks in a month.

December

Sunday	Monday	Tuesday	Wednesday	Thursday	Friday	Saturday
1	2	3	4	5	6	7
8	9	10	11	12	13	14
15	16	17	18	19	20	21
22	23	24	25	26	27	28
29	30	31				

DIRECTIONS Look at the calendar. Point to each date as you count. Talk about the days in a week and the full weeks in this month. Color the second week of this month.

Virginia SOL Success • 11.5e

forty-nine 49

August

Sunday	Monday	Tuesday	Wednesday	Thursday	Friday	Saturday
				1	2	3
4	5	6	7	8	9	10
11	12	13	14	15	16	17
18	19	20	21	22	23	24
25	26	27	28	29	30	31

1. 4

5

6

2. 4

5

6

3. Sunday

Monday

Tuesday

4. August 13

August 16

August 19

DIRECTIONS Look at the calendar. Circle your answer. **1.** How many Mondays are in this month? **2.** How many Fridays are in this month? **3.** What day of the week is August 6? **4.** What date is one week after August 9?

50 fifty

5

November

Sunday	Monday	Tuesday	Wednesday	Thursday	Friday	Saturday
					1	2
3	4	5	6	7	8	9
10	11	12	13	14	15	16
17	18	19	20	21	22	23
24	25	26	27	28	29	30

DIRECTIONS **5.** Use red to color the name of the month. Use yellow to color the names of the days of the week. Use green to color the third Monday of the month. Use blue to color the fourth Friday of the month.

Virginia SOL Success • 11.5e

Problem Solving · Applications

6

November

Sunday	Monday	Tuesday	Wednesday	Thursday	Friday	Saturday
					1	2
3	4	5	6	7	8	9
10	11	12	13	14	15	16
17	18	19	20	21	22	23
24	25	26	27	28	29	30

December

Sunday	Monday	Tuesday	Wednesday	Thursday	Friday	Saturday
1	2	3	4	5	6	7
8	9	10	11	12	13	14
15	16	17	18	19	20	21
22	23	24	25	26	27	28
29	30	31				

Sunday   Monday   Tuesday   Wednesday
Thursday   Friday   Saturday

7

DIRECTIONS **6.** If the last day of the month is Saturday, what will be the first day of the next month? Circle that day. **7.** Draw to show an activity you like to do in one of these months.

HOME ACTIVITY • Have your child tell you what day of the week it will be one week from today.

Weeks in a Month

Learning Objective You will understand time such as the weeks in a month.

September

Sunday	Monday	Tuesday	Wednesday	Thursday	Friday	Saturday
1	2	3	4	5	6	7
8	9	10	11	12	13	14
15	16	17	18	19	20	21
22	23	24	25	26	27	28
29	30					

DIRECTIONS 1. Use orange to color the name of the month. Use red to color the names of the days of the week. Use yellow to color the second Tuesday of the month. Use green to color the fourth week of the month.

Lesson Check

1

SEPTEMBER						
Sunday	Monday	Tuesday	Wednesday	Thursday	Friday	Saturday
1	2	3	4	5	6	7

Sunday   Monday   Tuesday   Wednesday

○   ○   ○   ○

Spiral Review

2

Sunday   Monday   Tuesday   Wednesday   Thursday   Friday   Saturday

Monday   Tuesday   Wednesday   Thursday

○   ○   ○   ○

3

_____

- - - - - -

_____

○   ○   ○   ○

DIRECTIONS **1.** Which day is the third day of September? Mark under your answer. **2.** Which day is two days after Tuesday? Mark under your answer. **3.** Count and tell how many cubes are in the cube train. Write the number. Mark under the cube train that is longer.

Name _____

Months in a Year

Essential Question How can you understand time such as the months in a year?

Learning Objective You will understand time such as the months in a year.

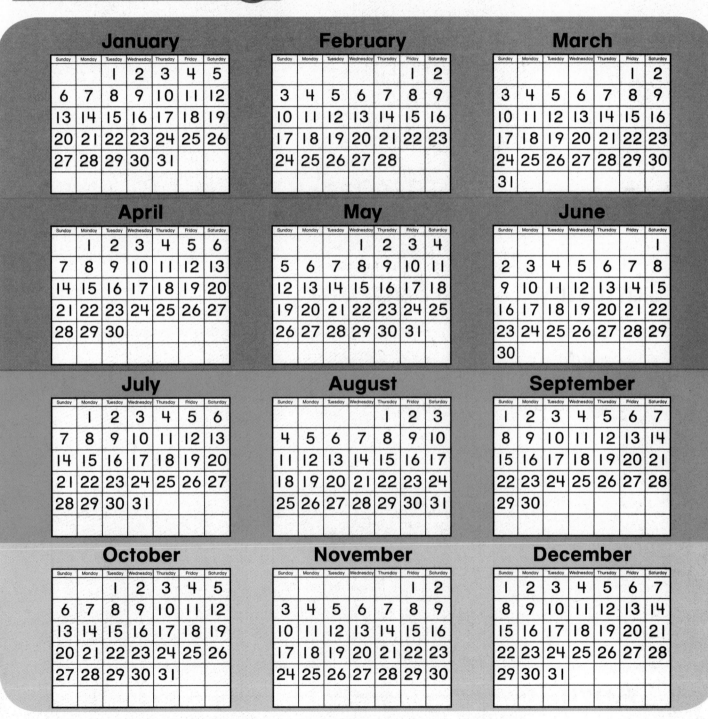

January
Sunday	Monday	Tuesday	Wednesday	Thursday	Friday	Saturday
		1	2	3	4	5
6	7	8	9	10	11	12
13	14	15	16	17	18	19
20	21	22	23	24	25	26
27	28	29	30	31		

February
Sunday	Monday	Tuesday	Wednesday	Thursday	Friday	Saturday
					1	2
3	4	5	6	7	8	9
10	11	12	13	14	15	16
17	18	19	20	21	22	23
24	25	26	27	28		

March
Sunday	Monday	Tuesday	Wednesday	Thursday	Friday	Saturday
					1	2
3	4	5	6	7	8	9
10	11	12	13	14	15	16
17	18	19	20	21	22	23
24	25	26	27	28	29	30
31						

April
Sunday	Monday	Tuesday	Wednesday	Thursday	Friday	Saturday
	1	2	3	4	5	6
7	8	9	10	11	12	13
14	15	16	17	18	19	20
21	22	23	24	25	26	27
28	29	30				

May
Sunday	Monday	Tuesday	Wednesday	Thursday	Friday	Saturday
			1	2	3	4
5	6	7	8	9	10	11
12	13	14	15	16	17	18
19	20	21	22	23	24	25
26	27	28	29	30	31	

June
Sunday	Monday	Tuesday	Wednesday	Thursday	Friday	Saturday
						1
2	3	4	5	6	7	8
9	10	11	12	13	14	15
16	17	18	19	20	21	22
23	24	25	26	27	28	29
30						

July
Sunday	Monday	Tuesday	Wednesday	Thursday	Friday	Saturday
	1	2	3	4	5	6
7	8	9	10	11	12	13
14	15	16	17	18	19	20
21	22	23	24	25	26	27
28	29	30	31			

August
Sunday	Monday	Tuesday	Wednesday	Thursday	Friday	Saturday
				1	2	3
4	5	6	7	8	9	10
11	12	13	14	15	16	17
18	19	20	21	22	23	24
25	26	27	28	29	30	31

September
Sunday	Monday	Tuesday	Wednesday	Thursday	Friday	Saturday
1	2	3	4	5	6	7
8	9	10	11	12	13	14
15	16	17	18	19	20	21
22	23	24	25	26	27	28
29	30					

October
Sunday	Monday	Tuesday	Wednesday	Thursday	Friday	Saturday
		1	2	3	4	5
6	7	8	9	10	11	12
13	14	15	16	17	18	19
20	21	22	23	24	25	26
27	28	29	30	31		

November
Sunday	Monday	Tuesday	Wednesday	Thursday	Friday	Saturday
					1	2
3	4	5	6	7	8	9
10	11	12	13	14	15	16
17	18	19	20	21	22	23
24	25	26	27	28	29	30

December
Sunday	Monday	Tuesday	Wednesday	Thursday	Friday	Saturday
1	2	3	4	5	6	7
8	9	10	11	12	13	14
15	16	17	18	19	20	21
22	23	24	25	26	27	28
29	30	31				

DIRECTIONS Point to the months as you say them in order. Count to find out how many months are in one year. Circle the month it is now.

January	February	March	April	May	June

① January   February   March

② April   May   June

DIRECTIONS 1. Trace the circle around the month that comes between January and March. 2. Circle the month that comes after May.

Name _____

| July | August | September | October | November | December |

3

July   August   September

4

October   November   December

DIRECTIONS **3.** Circle the month that comes between July and September. **4.** Circle the month that comes before November.

Problem Solving • Applications Real World

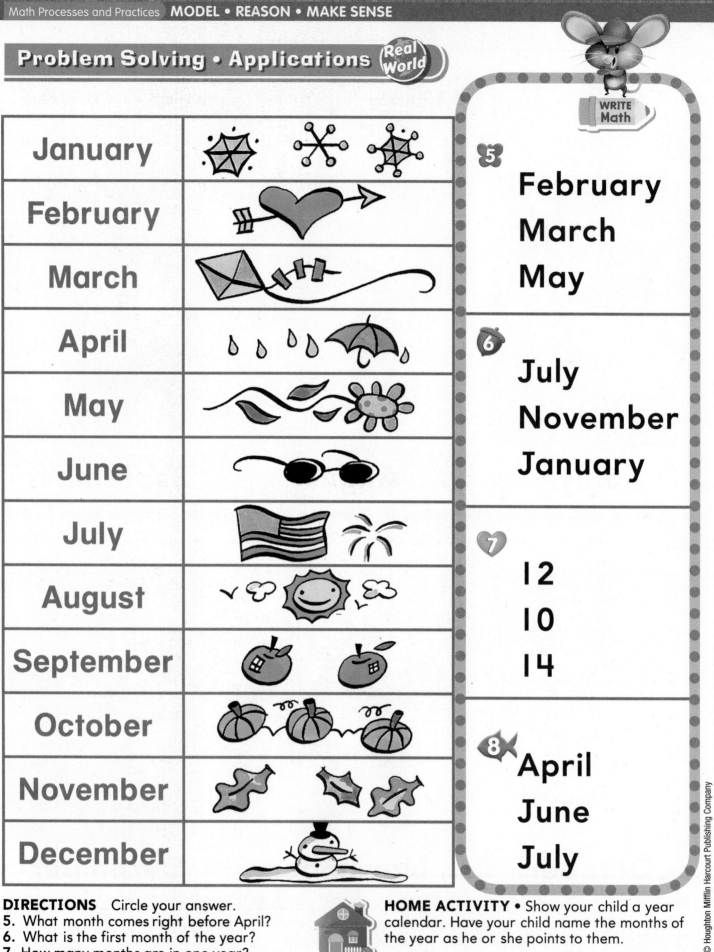

WRITE Math

January	
February	
March	
April	
May	
June	
July	
August	
September	
October	
November	
December	

5. February
   March
   May

6. July
   November
   January

7. 12
   10
   14

8. April
   June
   July

DIRECTIONS Circle your answer.
5. What month comes right before April?
6. What is the first month of the year?
7. How many months are in one year?
8. What month comes right after May?

HOME ACTIVITY • Show your child a year calendar. Have your child name the months of the year as he or she points to them.

58 fifty-eight

Months in a Year

Learning Objective You will understand time using months in a year.

January	February	March	April	May	June

1

January   February   March

- -

2

April   May   June

DIRECTIONS   1. Circle the month that comes right before February.   **2.** Circle the month that comes between April and June.

Lesson Check

1 January   February   _____

December   March   April   May
   ○   ○   ○   ○

---

2   September   November   August
             ○   ○   ○

Spiral Review

3

SEPTEMBER						
Sunday	Monday	Tuesday	Wednesday	Thursday	Friday	Saturday
1	2	3	4	5	6	7

Sunday   Monday   Tuesday Wednesday
   ○   ○   ○   ○

4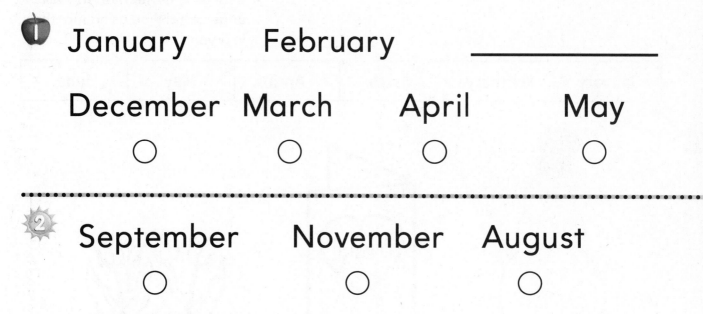

   7   8   9   10
   ○   ○   ○   ○

DIRECTIONS 1. Which month comes right after February? Mark under your answer. 2. Which month comes right before October? Mark under your answer. 3. What day is the third day of September? Mark under your answer. 4. How many cherries are left? Mark under your answer.

Name _____

Identify a Penny

Essential Question How can you identify a penny?

Learning Objective You will identify a penny.

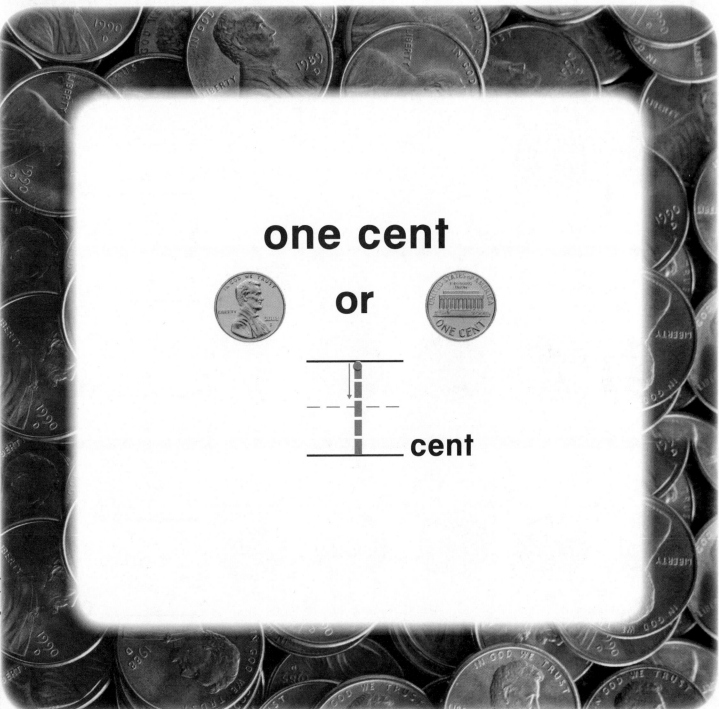

one cent

or

_____
cent

DIRECTIONS Place a penny to match each one shown. Tell what is alike about the pennies. Tell what is different about the pennies. Trace the number that shows the value of a penny.

Virginia SOL Success • 11.5g

sixty-one 61

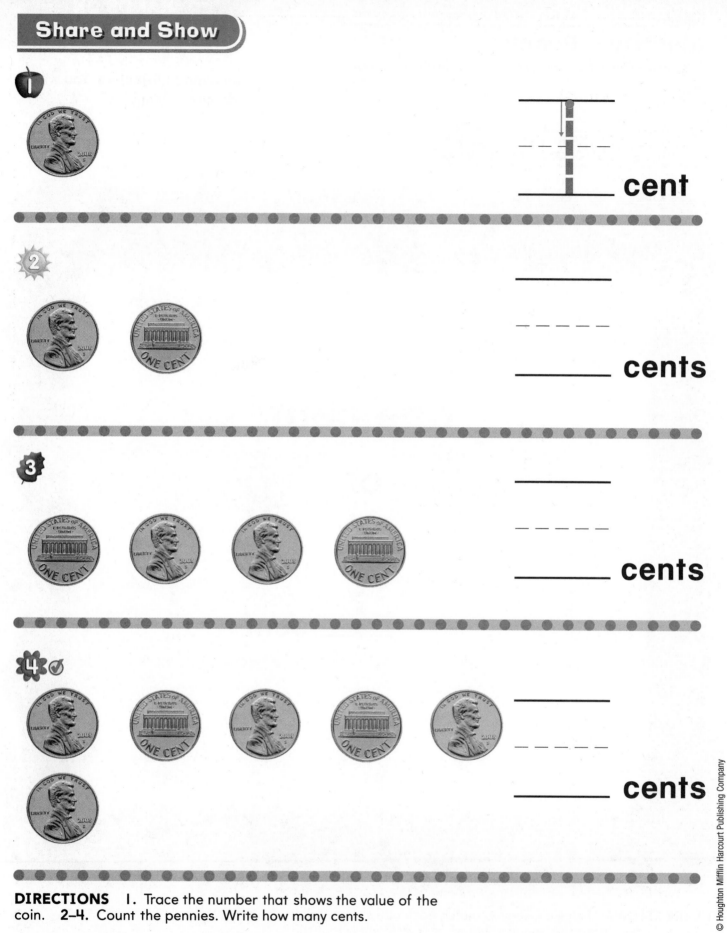

1 ___ cent

2 _____ cents

3 _____ cents

4 _____ cents

DIRECTIONS 1. Trace the number that shows the value of the coin. 2–4. Count the pennies. Write how many cents.

Name _____

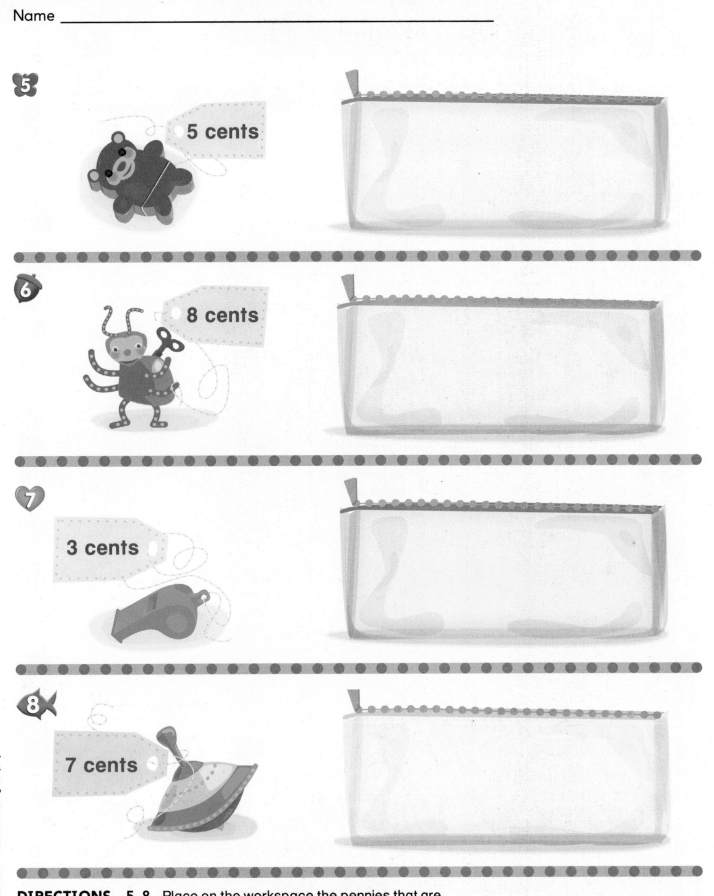

5 5 cents

6 8 cents

7 3 cents

8 7 cents

DIRECTIONS 5–8. Place on the workspace the pennies that are
needed to buy the toy. Draw the pennies.

Virginia SOL Success • 11.5g

Problem Solving • Applications

9

10

DIRECTIONS 9. Julian buys a toy for 3 cents. Draw the coins he needs to buy the toy. **10.** Draw to show what you know about a penny.

HOME ACTIVITY • Show your child 1 to 10 pennies. Have him or her count the pennies and tell their value.

Identify a Penny

Learning Objective You will identify a penny.

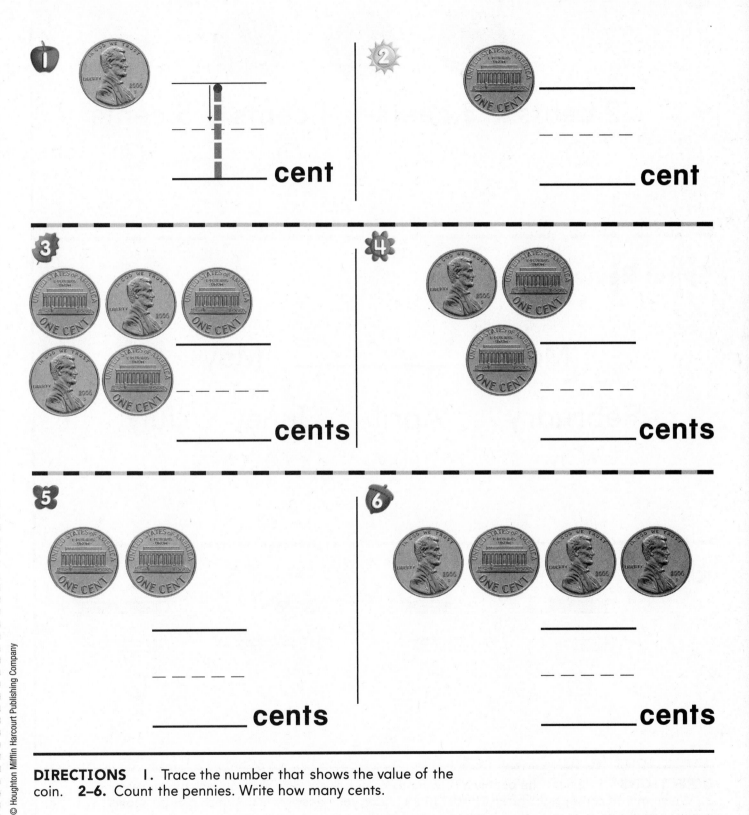

① ____ cent

② _____ cent

③ _____ cents

④ _____ cents

⑤ _____ cents

⑥ _____ cents

DIRECTIONS **1.** Trace the number that shows the value of the coin. **2–6.** Count the pennies. Write how many cents.

Lesson Check

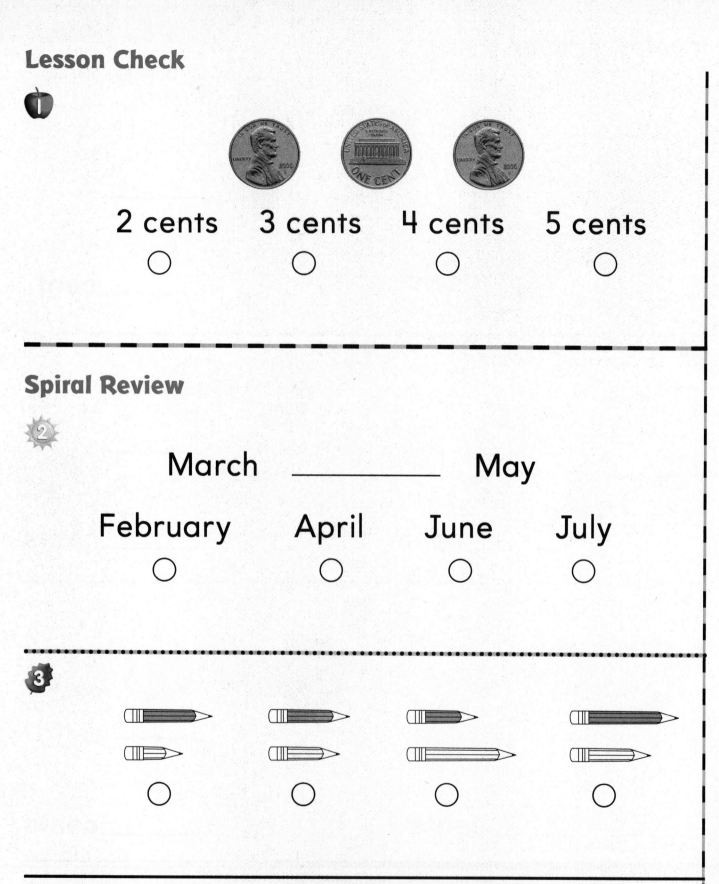

2 cents   3 cents   4 cents   5 cents
  ○   ○   ○   ○

Spiral Review

March _____ May

February   April   June   July
  ○   ○   ○   ○

DIRECTIONS 1. Count the pennies. How many cents are shown? Mark under your answer.
2. Which month comes right after March? Mark under your answer.   3. Which picture shows
a gray pencil that is shorter than a white pencil? Mark under your answer.

Name _____

Identify a Nickel and Its Value

Essential Question How can you identify a nickel and its value?

Learning Objective You will identify a nickel and its value.

Listen and Draw *Real World*

five cents

or

5 cents

DIRECTIONS Place a nickel to match each one shown. Tell what is alike about the nickels. Tell what is different about the nickels. Trace the number that shows the value of a nickel.

Virginia SOL Success • 11.5h

Share and Show

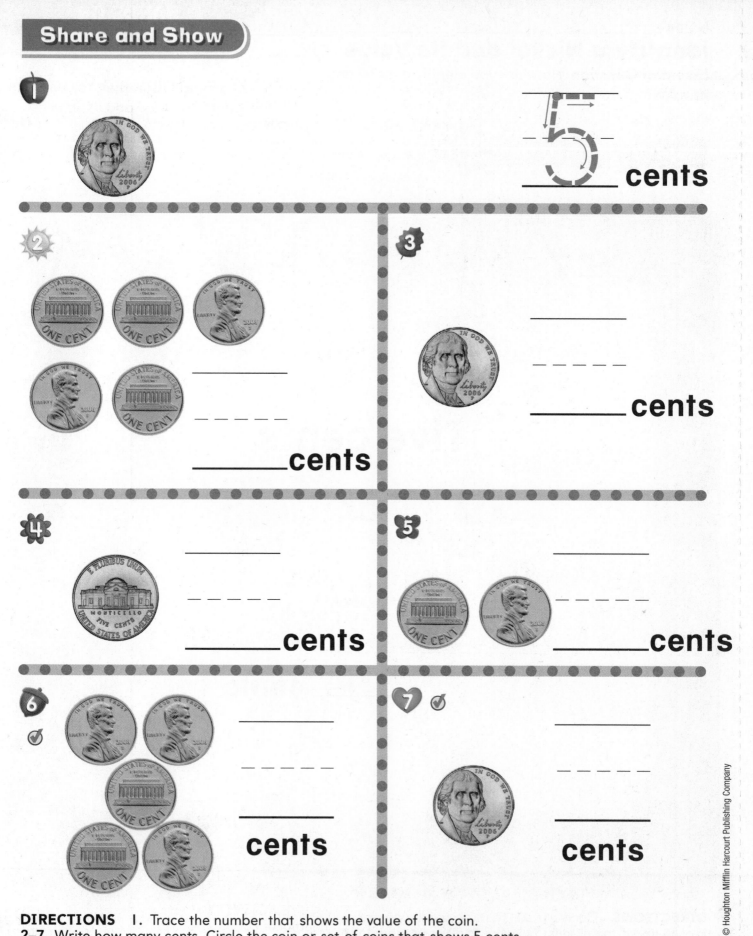

1

_____ cents

2

_____ cents

3

_____ cents

4

_____ cents

5

_____ cents

6

_____ cents

7

_____ cents

DIRECTIONS 1. Trace the number that shows the value of the coin.
2–7. Write how many cents. Circle the coin or set of coins that shows 5 cents.

Name _____

8 4 cents

9 5 cents

10 3 cents

11 5 cents

DIRECTIONS 8–11 Place the coin or coins on the workspace that are needed to buy the toy. Draw the coins.

HOME ACTIVITY • Show your child a handful of coins that includes nickels. Have him or her identify each nickel. Now have your child use pennies to show the value of a nickel.

Problem Solving • Applications

12

13

DIRECTIONS **12.** Jesse buys a toy boat for 5 cents. Draw the coin or coins he needs to buy the toy. **13.** Draw to show what you know about a nickel.

HOME ACTIVITY • Show your child 5 pennies. Have him or her count the pennies and tell their value.

70 seventy

Name _____

Identify a Nickel and Its Value

Learning Objective You will identify a nickel and its value.

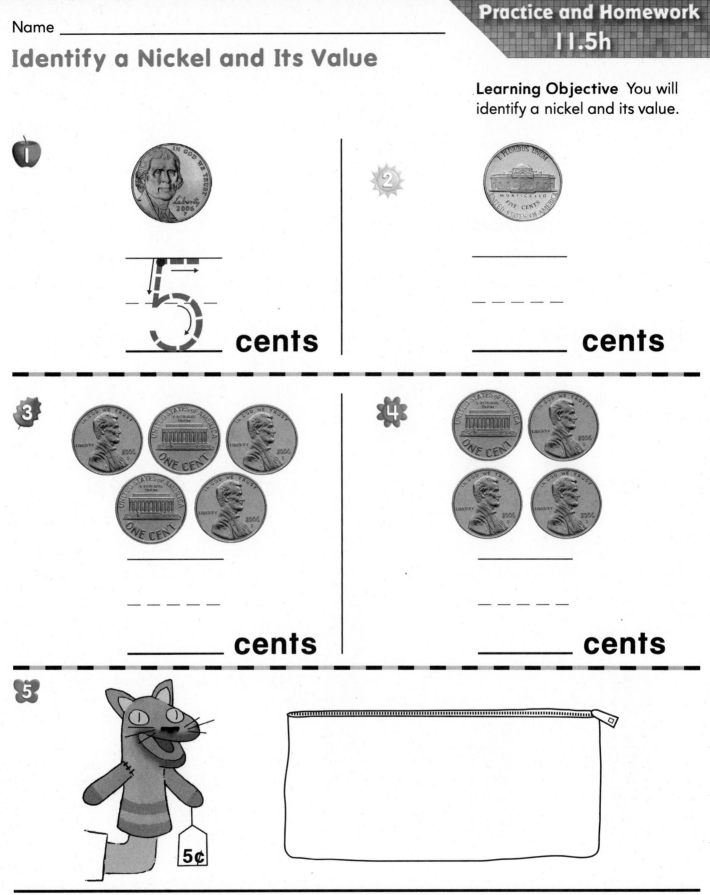

1 _____ 5 cents

2 _____ cents

3 _____ cents

4 _____ cents

5 5¢

DIRECTIONS 1. Trace the number that shows the value of the coin. 2–4. Write how many cents. Circle the coin or set of coins that shows 5 cents. 5. Place the coin or coins on the workspace that are needed to buy the toy. Draw the coins.

Virginia SOL Success • 11.5h

Lesson Check

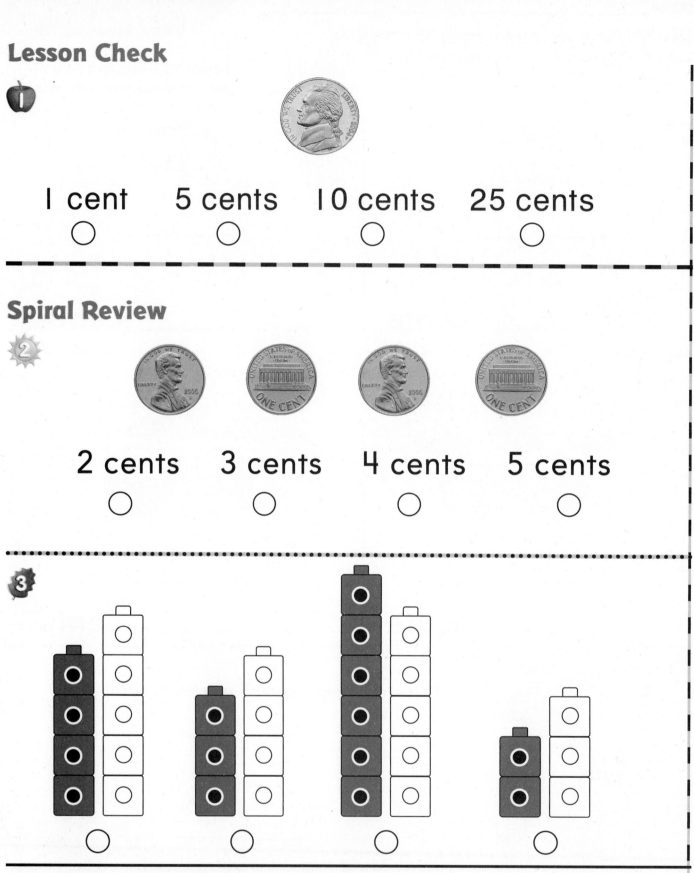

1

1 cent   5 cents   10 cents   25 cents
○   ○   ○   ○

Spiral Review

2

2 cents   3 cents   4 cents   5 cents
○   ○   ○   ○

3

○   ○   ○   ○

DIRECTIONS 1. Which shows the value of the coin? Mark under your answer. 2. Count the pennies. How many cents are shown? Mark under your answer. 3. Which picture shows the gray cube tower that is taller than the white cube tower? Mark under your answer.

Name _____

Identify a Dime and Its Value

Essential Question How can you identify a dime and its value?

Lesson Objective You will identify a dime and its value.

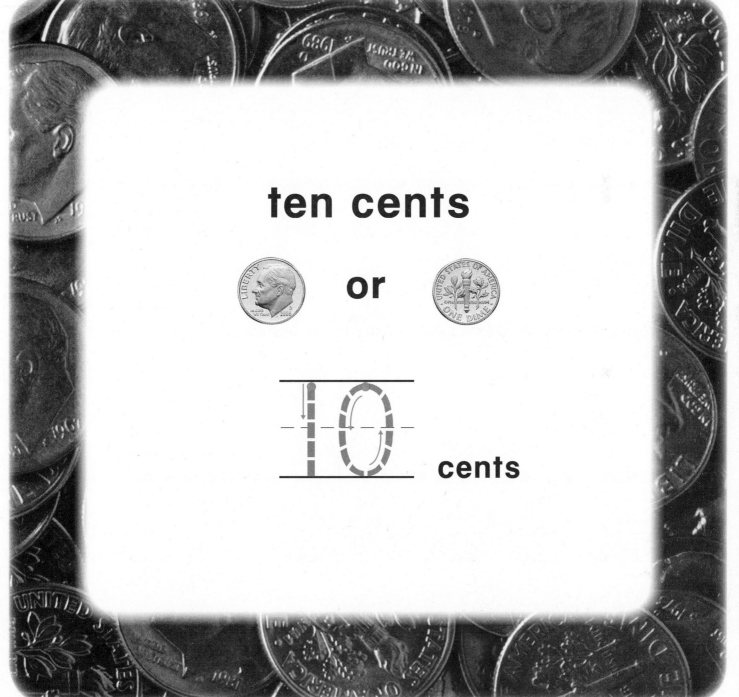

ten cents

or

10 cents

DIRECTIONS Place a dime to match each one shown. Tell what is alike about the dimes. Tell what is different about the dimes. Trace the number that shows the value of a dime.

Virginia SOL Success • 11.5i

Share and Show

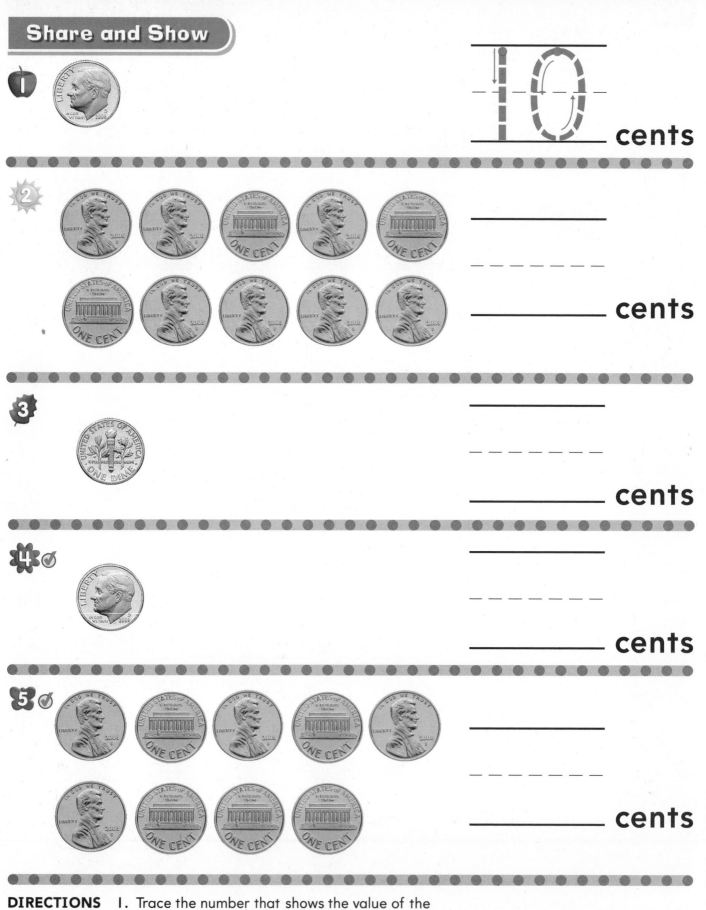

1 10 cents

2 _____ cents

3 _____ cents

4 _____ cents

5 _____ cents

DIRECTIONS **1.** Trace the number that shows the value of the coin. **2–5.** Write how many cents. Circle the coin or set of coins that shows 10 cents.

6 · 8 cents

7 · 10 cents

8 · 9 cents

DIRECTIONS 6–8. Place on the workspace the coin or coins that are needed to buy the toy. Draw the coin or coins.

Problem Solving • Applications

9

10

DIRECTIONS **9.** Peyton buys an apple for 10 cents. Draw the coin or coins she needs to buy the apple. **10.** Draw to show what you know about a dime.

HOME ACTIVITY • Show your child a handful of coins that includes dimes. Have him or her identify each dime. Now have your child use pennies to show the value of a dime.

Identify a Dime and Its Value

Learning Objective You will identify a dime and its value.

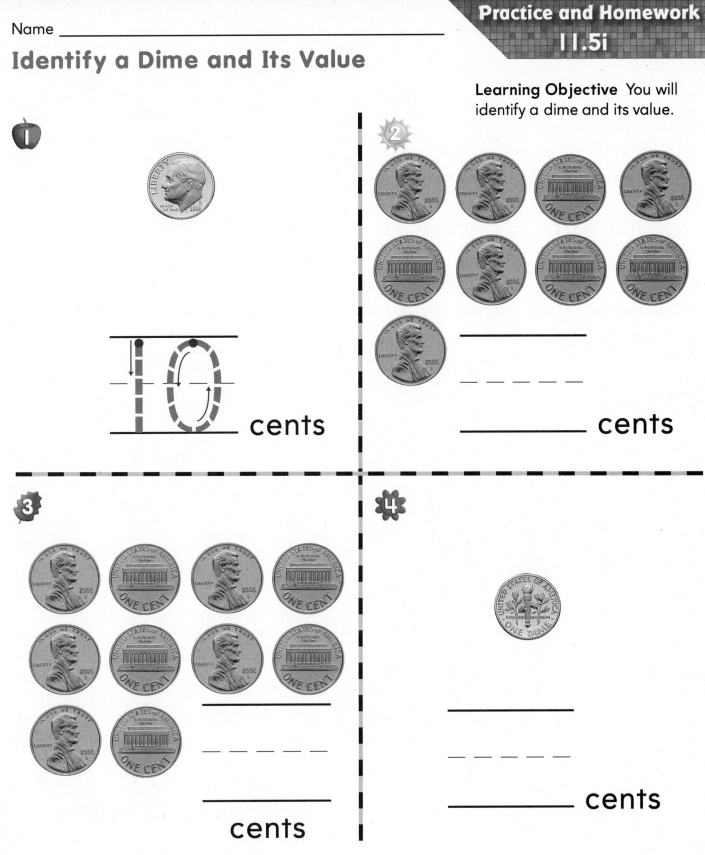

①

___ 10 cents

②

_____ cents

③

_____ cents

④

_____ cents

DIRECTIONS **1.** Trace the number that shows the value of the coin. **2–4.** Write how many cents. Circle the coin or set of coins that shows 10 cents.

Lesson Check

1

I cent	5 cents	10 cents	25 cents
○	○	○	○

Spiral Review

2

| ○ | ○ | ○ | ○ |

3

I cent	5 cents	10 cents	25 cents
○	○	○	○

DIRECTIONS 1. Which shows the value of the coin? Mark under your answer. 2. Which object is heavier than the book? Mark under your answer. 3. Which shows the value of the coin? Mark under your answer.

Name _____

Identify a Quarter and Its Value
Essential Question How can you identify a quarter and its value?

Lesson Objective You will identify a quarter and its value.

twenty-five cents

or

25 cents

DIRECTIONS Place a quarter to match each one shown. Tell what is alike about the quarters. Tell what is different about the quarters. Trace the number that shows the value of a quarter.

Virginia SOL Success • 11.5j

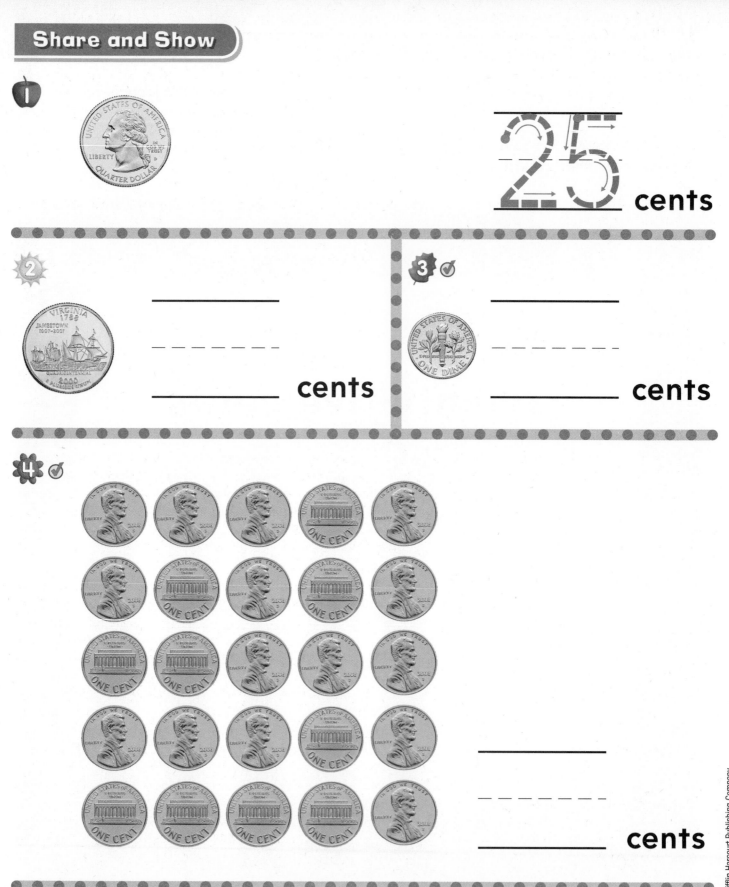

1 2̲5̲ **cents**

2 _____
_ _ _ _ _ _ _ _ _
_____ **cents**

3 _____
_ _ _ _ _ _ _ _ _
_____ **cents**

4 _____
_ _ _ _ _ _ _ _ _
_____ **cents**

DIRECTIONS 1. Trace the number that shows the value of the
coin. **2–4.** Write how many cents. Circle the coin or set of coins
that shows 25 cents.

5

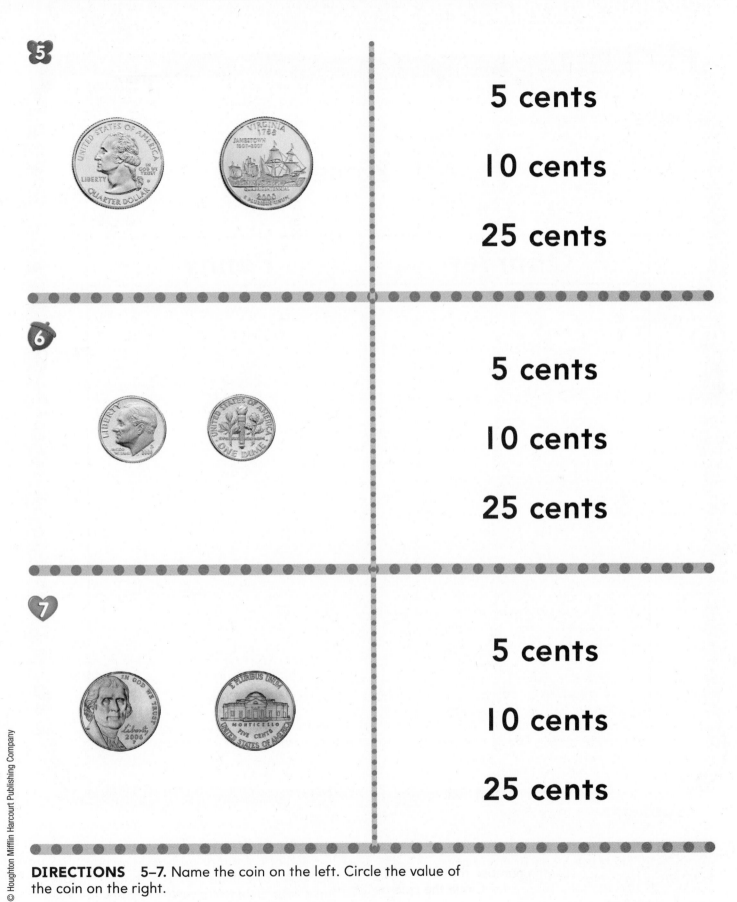

5 cents

10 cents

25 cents

6

5 cents

10 cents

25 cents

7

5 cents

10 cents

25 cents

DIRECTIONS 5–7. Name the coin on the left. Circle the value of the coin on the right.

Problem Solving • Applications Real World

25 cents

Quarter	Penny

DIRECTIONS 8. How many ways can you show 25 cents using only one kind of coin? Draw and color the coins.

HOME ACTIVITY • Show your child a handful of coins that includes quarters. Have him or her identify each quarter. Now have your child use pennies to show the value of a quarter.

Name _____

Identify a Quarter and its Value

Learning Objective You will identify a quarter and its value.

1

 **cents**

2

_____

- - - - - - - - - - - - - -

_____ **cents**

DIRECTIONS **1.** Trace the number that shows the value of the coin. **2.** Write how many cents. Circle the coin or set of coins that shows 25 cents.

© Houghton Mifflin Harcourt Publishing Company

Lesson Check

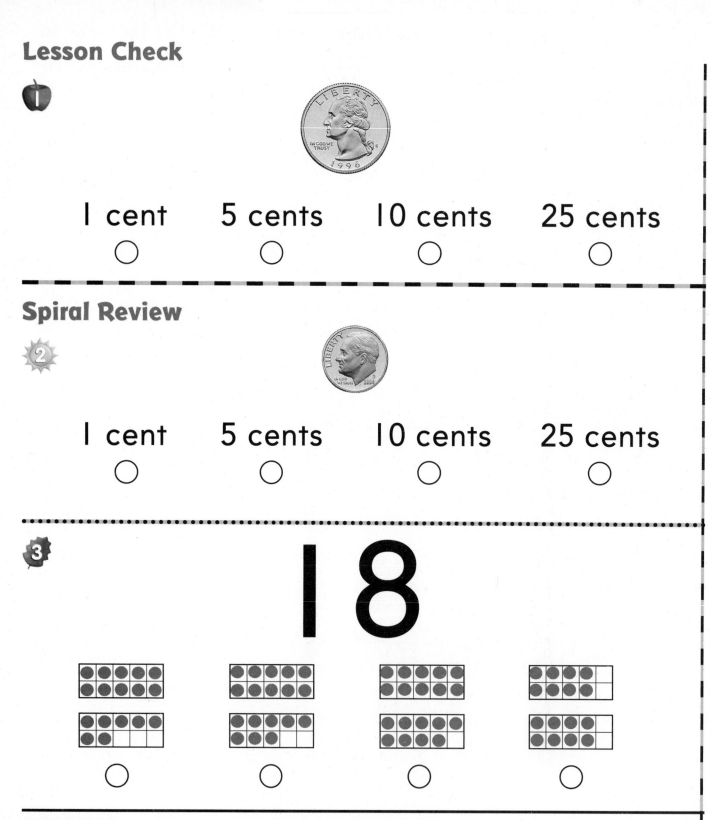

1

1 cent　　5 cents　　10 cents　　25 cents
　○　　　　○　　　　　○　　　　　○

Spiral Review

2

1 cent　　5 cents　　10 cents　　25 cents
　○　　　　○　　　　　○　　　　　○

3

18

○　　　　　○　　　　　○　　　　　○

DIRECTIONS 1. Which shows the value of the coin? Mark under your answer. 2. Which shows the value of the coin? Mark under your answer. 3. Which ten frame shows 17? Mark under your answer.

Name _____

Algebra • Identify and Describe a Pattern

Essential Question How can you identify and describe a pattern?

Learning Objective You will identify and describe a pattern.

Listen and Draw *Real World*

DIRECTIONS Point to each shape as you describe the pattern. Which part of the pattern repeats again and again? Use shapes to copy the pattern. Trace the shapes.

Virginia SOL Success • 12.5a

eighty-five **85**

Share and Show

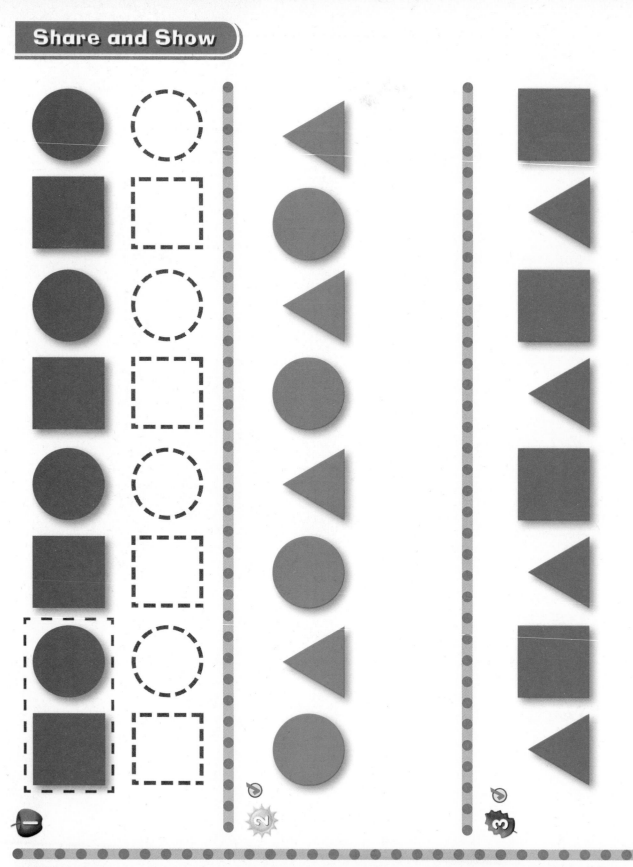

DIRECTIONS Identify the pattern. Read to describe the pattern. Which part of the pattern repeats again and again? **1.** Trace the box around the part of the pattern that repeats. Place shapes to copy the pattern. Trace the pattern. **2–3.** Draw a box around the part of the pattern that repeats. Place shapes to copy the pattern. Draw and color the pattern.

86 eighty-six

Name _____

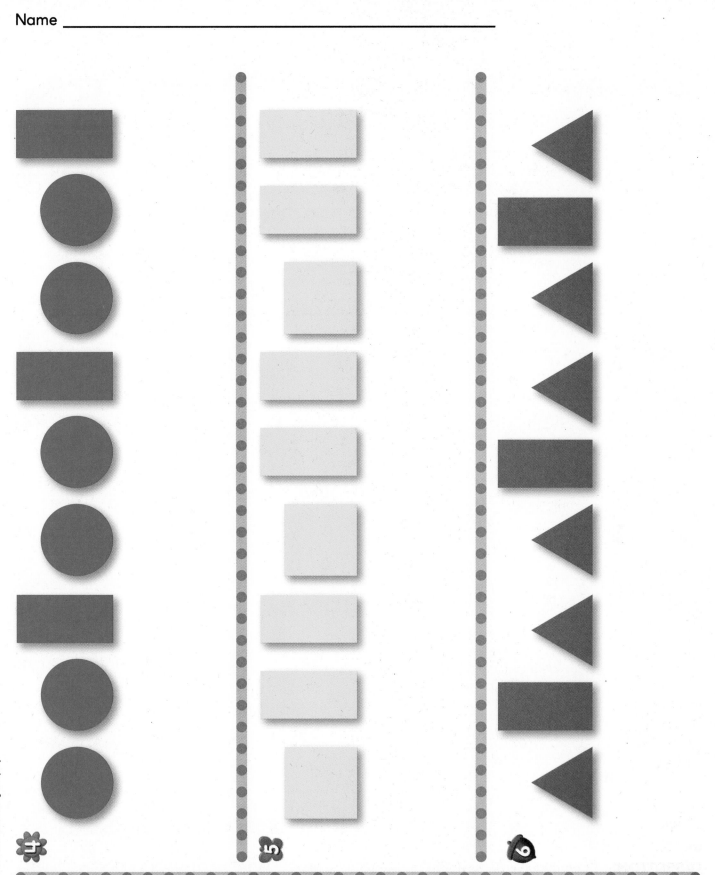

DIRECTIONS 4–6. Identify the pattern. Read to describe the pattern. Which part of the pattern repeats again and again? Draw a box around that part. Place shapes to copy the pattern. Draw and color the pattern.

Virginia SOL Success • 12.5a

Problem Solving • Applications

7

8

DIRECTIONS **7.** Identify the pattern. Which shape is unknown in the pattern? Draw and color the shape where it belongs.   Draw a box around the part of the pattern that repeats again and again. **8.** Draw and color to show what you know about a shape pattern.

HOME ACTIVITY • Have your child use household objects to show you a shape pattern.

Name _____

Algebra • Identify and Describe a Pattern

Learning Objective You will identify and describe a pattern.

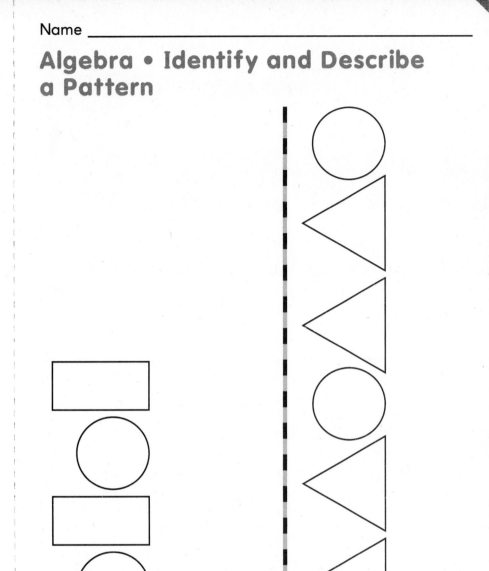

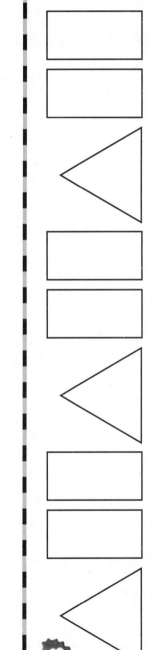

DIRECTIONS 1–3. Identify the pattern. Read to describe the pattern. Which part of the pattern repeats again and again? Draw a box around that part. Place shapes to copy the pattern. Draw and color the pattern.

Virginia SOL Success • 12.5a

eighty-nine **89**

Lesson Check

1

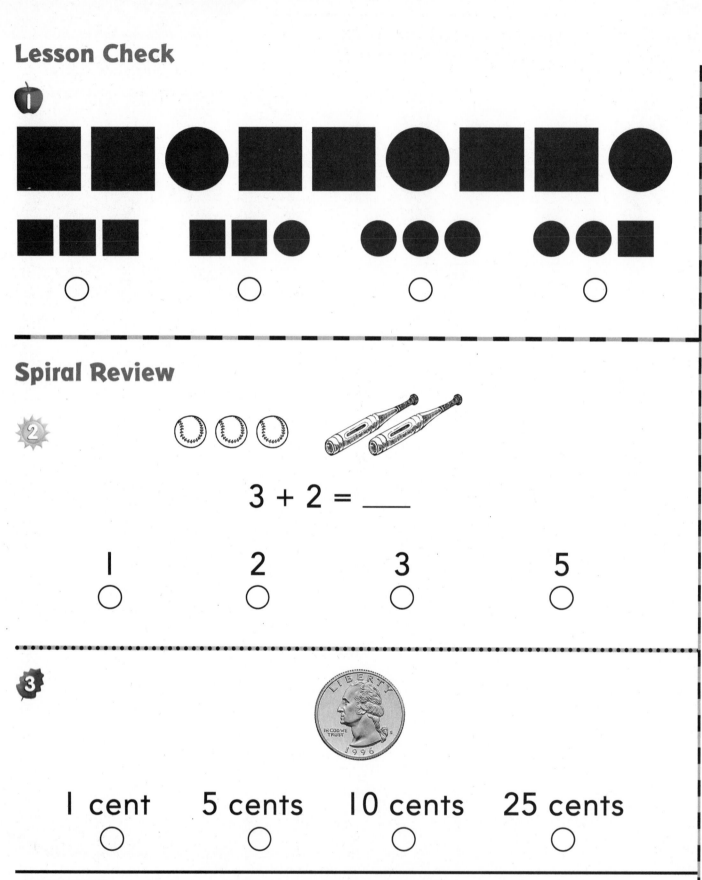

○   ○   ○   ○

Spiral Review

2

3 + 2 = ___

1   2   3   5

○   ○   ○   ○

3

1 cent   5 cents   10 cents   25 cents

○   ○   ○   ○

DIRECTIONS 1. Which set of shapes shows the pattern? Mark under your answer. **2.** How many objects in all? Mark under your answer. **3.** Which shows the value of the coin? Mark under your answer.

Name _____

Algebra • Extend a Pattern

Essential Question How can you extend a pattern?

Learning Objective You will extend a pattern.

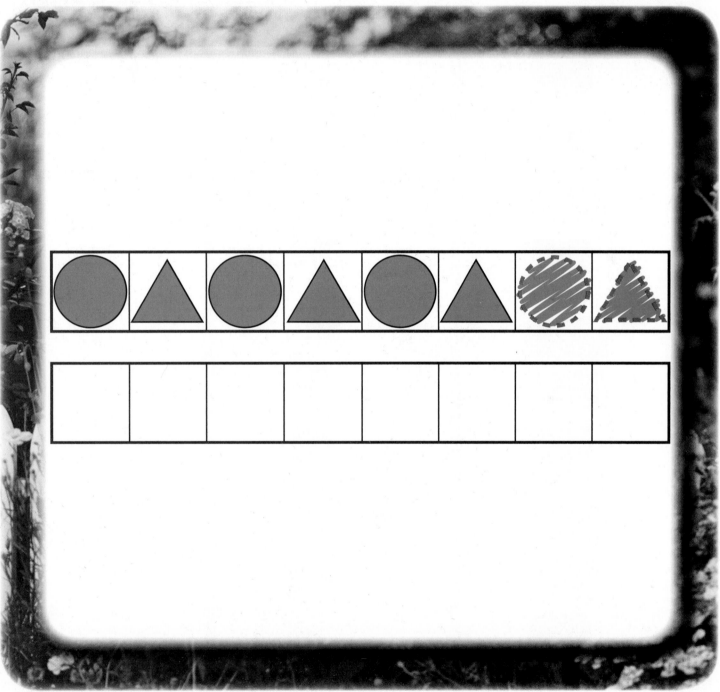

DIRECTIONS Place shapes as shown on the first 6 shapes. Describe the pattern. Which shapes would most likely come next? Place those shapes as shown. Trace the shapes. Use shapes to copy the pattern. Point to each shape as you describe the pattern. Draw and color the shape pattern.

Virginia SOL Success • 12.5b

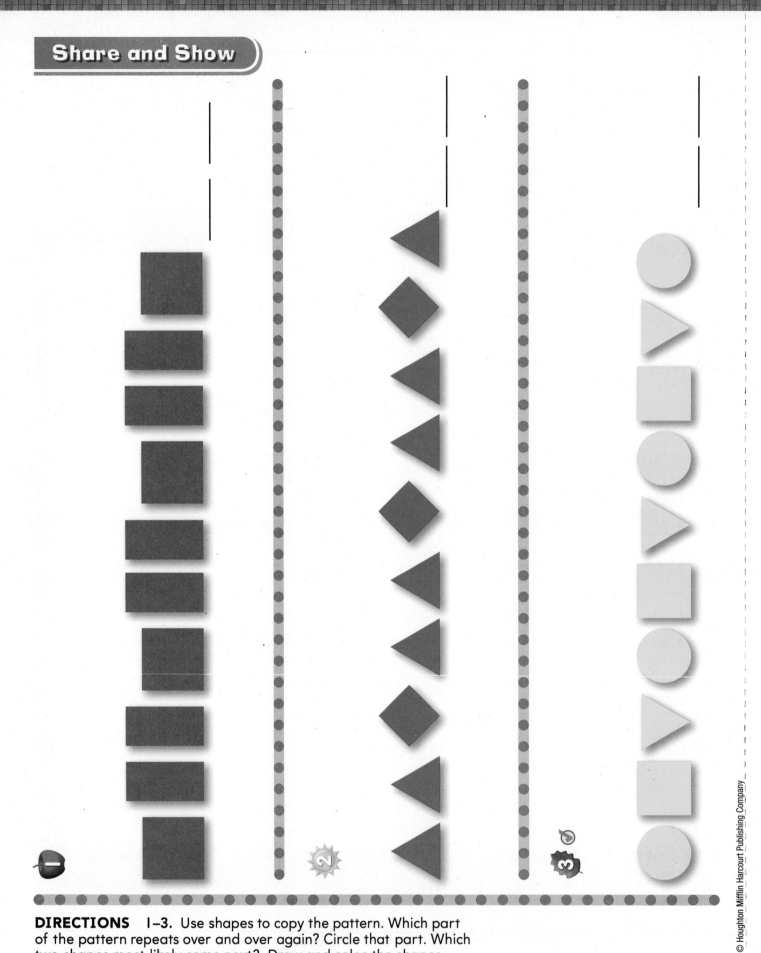

DIRECTIONS 1–3. Use shapes to copy the pattern. Which part of the pattern repeats over and over again? Circle that part. Which two shapes most likely come next? Draw and color the shapes.

Name _____

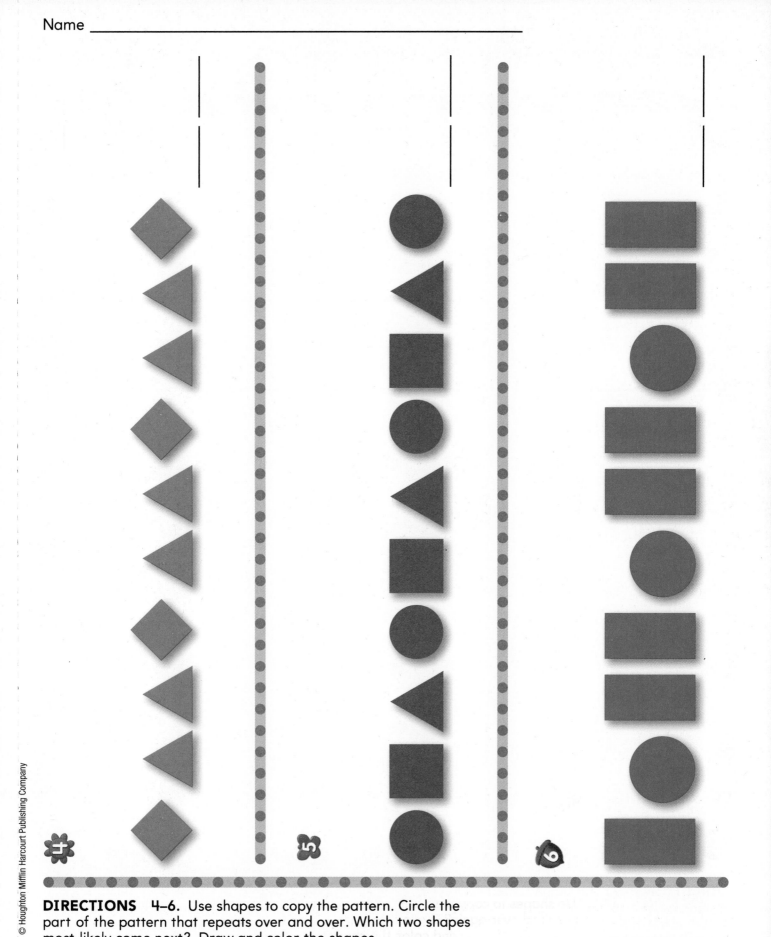

DIRECTIONS 4–6. Use shapes to copy the pattern. Circle the part of the pattern that repeats over and over. Which two shapes most likely come next? Draw and color the shapes.

Virginia SOL Success • 12.5b

ninety-three 93

Problem Solving • Applications Real World

❤ 7

⬛ ⬤ ___ ___ ___ ___

🐟 8

DIRECTIONS 7. The shape pattern is square, circle. Draw to extend the pattern. 8. Draw to show what you know about extending a shape pattern.

HOME ACTIVITY • Have your child use household objects to make a simple repeating shape pattern. Have him or her tell what would most likely come next in the pattern.

94 ninety-four

Name _____

Algebra • Extend a Pattern

Practice and Homework
12.5b

Learning Objective You will extend a pattern.

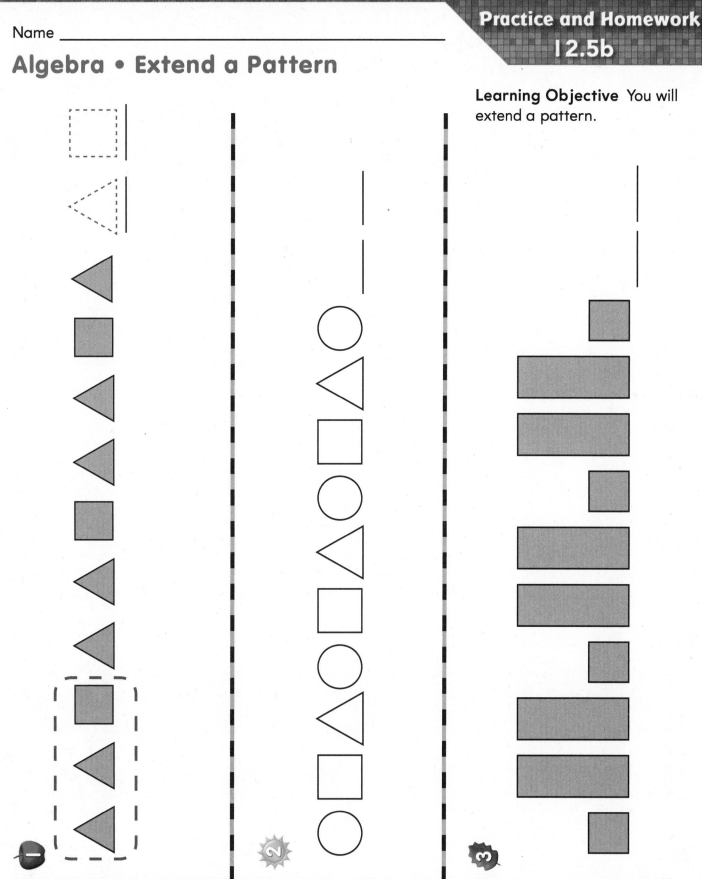

© Houghton Mifflin Harcourt Publishing Company

DIRECTIONS **1.** Use shapes to copy the pattern. Trace the circle to show which part of the pattern repeats. Trace to show the shapes that come next. **2–3.** Use shapes to copy the pattern. Circle the part of the pattern that repeats. Which two shapes most likely come next? Draw and color the shapes.

Virginia SOL Success • 12.5b

ninety-five **95**

Lesson Check

1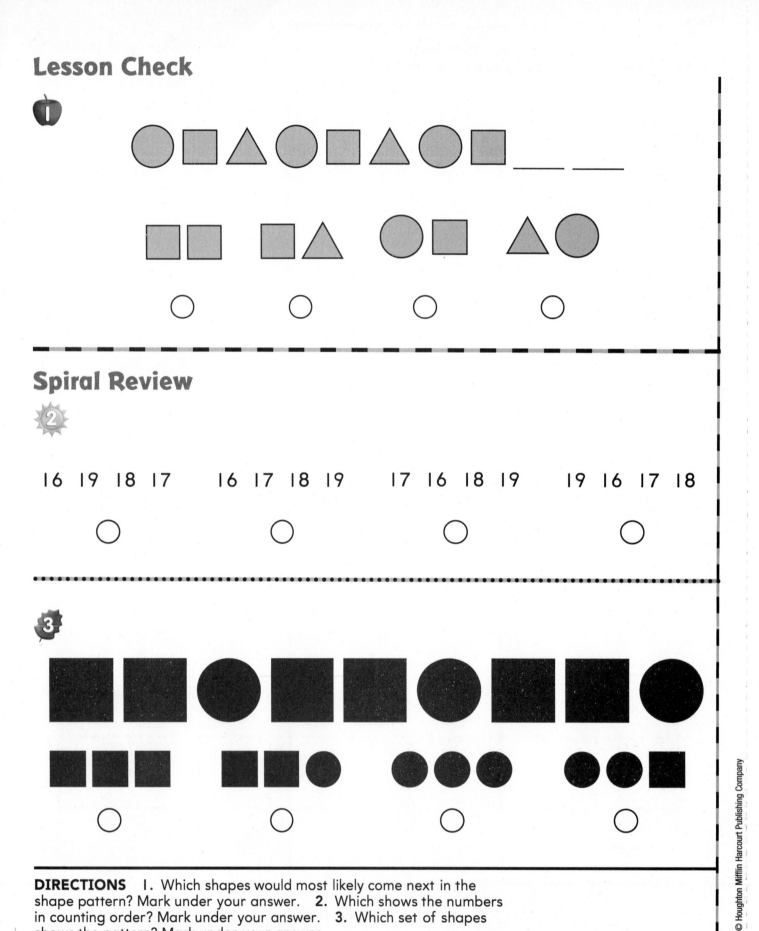

⬤ ⬛ ▲ ⬤ ⬛ ▲ ⬤ ⬛ ___ ___

⬛ ⬛   ⬛ ▲   ⬤ ⬛   ▲ ⬤

○   ○   ○   ○

Spiral Review

2

16 19 18 17   16 17 18 19   17 16 18 19   19 16 17 18

○   ○   ○   ○

3

○   ○   ○   ○

DIRECTIONS   1. Which shapes would most likely come next in the shape pattern? Mark under your answer.   2. Which shows the numbers in counting order? Mark under your answer.   3. Which set of shapes shows the pattern? Mark under your answer.

Name _____

Algebra • Create a Pattern

Essential Question How can you create a pattern?

Learning Objective You will create a pattern.

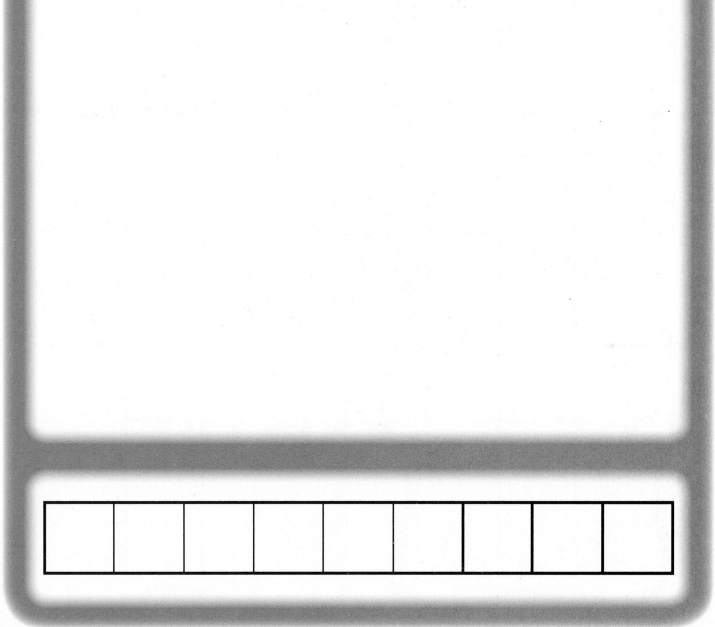

DIRECTIONS Place a handful of cubes in the workspace. Move the cubes to the pattern strip to create a pattern. Draw and color the pattern. Describe the pattern. Talk about the part that repeats again and again.

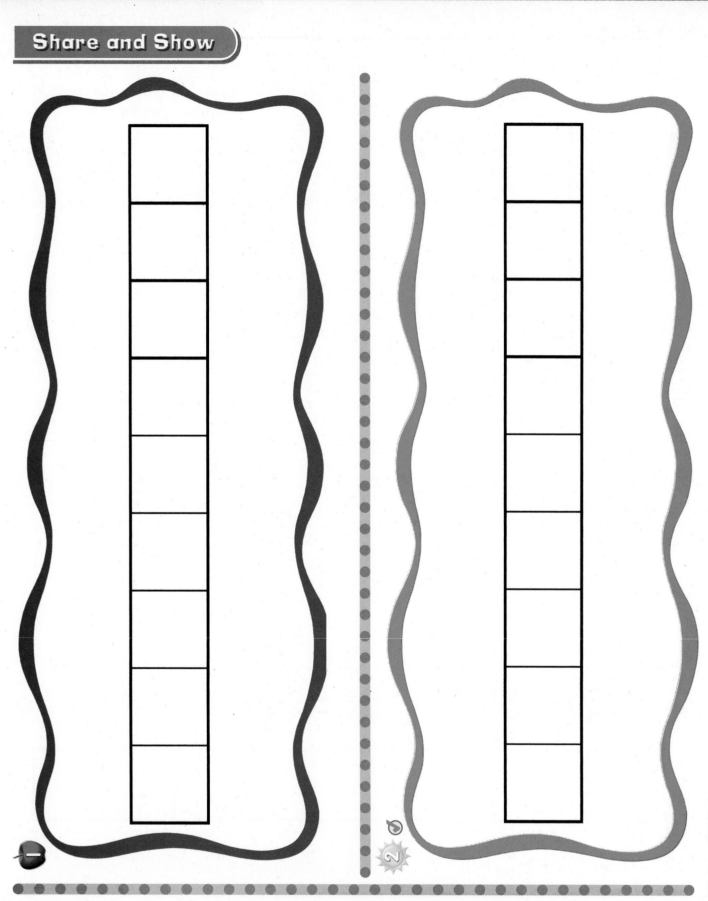

DIRECTIONS 1. Use counters to make a pattern. Draw and color your pattern. Circle the part that repeats again and again. 2. Use pattern blocks to make a pattern. Draw and color your pattern. Circle the part that repeats again and again.

Name _____

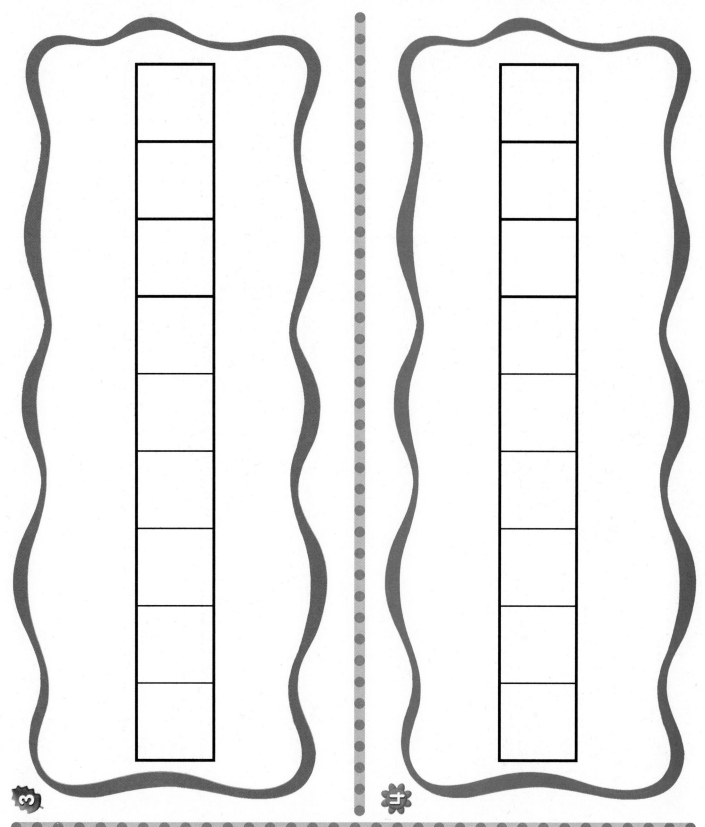

DIRECTIONS 3–4. Use shapes to create a pattern. Draw and
color your pattern. Circle the part that repeats again and again.
Describe your pattern to a friend.

Virginia SOL Success • 12.5c

ninety-nine **99**

Problem Solving • Applications Real World

WRITE Math

5

6

DIRECTIONS 5. Use objects to create a pattern. Draw and color the pattern. **6.** Draw to show what you know about creating a pattern.

Home Activity • Have your child use household objects such as macaroni, buttons, or coins to create a pattern. Have him or her describe the pattern.

Name _____

Algebra • Create a Pattern

Learning Objective You will create a pattern.

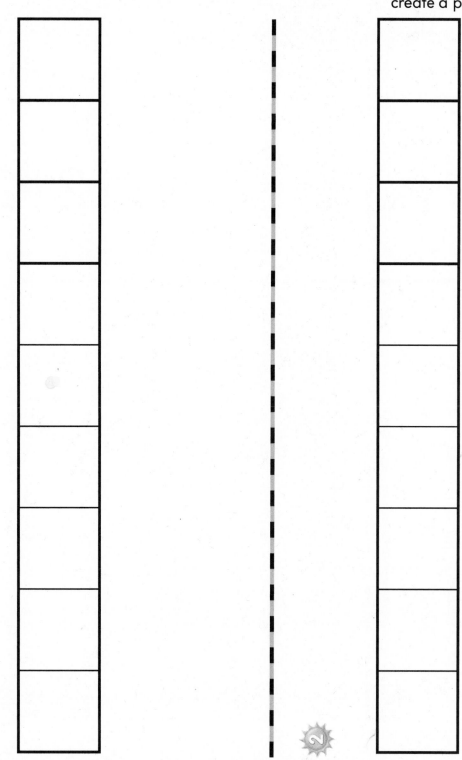

DIRECTIONS **1.** Use counters to make a pattern. Draw and color your pattern. Circle the part that repeats again and again. **2.** Use pattern blocks to make a pattern. Draw and color your pattern. Circle the part that repeats again and again.

Lesson Check

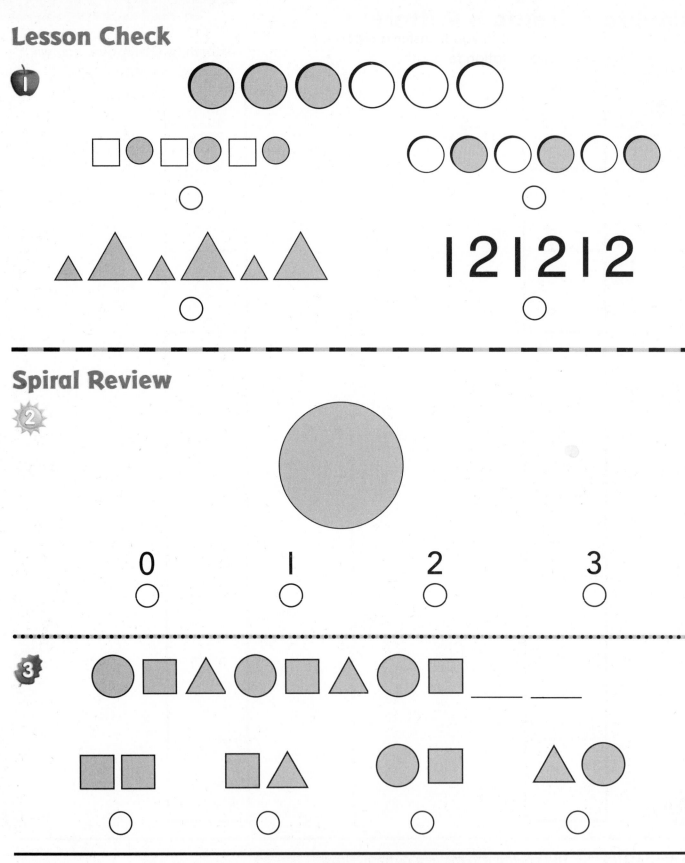

1 2 1 2 1 2

Spiral Review

0   1   2   3

DIRECTIONS   **1.** Which pattern could you create from these counters? Mark under your answer.   **2.** How many straight sides does the circle have? Mark under your answer.   **3.** Which shapes would most likely come next in the pattern? Mark under your answer.

102 one hundred two

Name _____

Algebra • Transfer a Pattern

Essential Question How can you transfer a repeating pattern from one representation to another?

Learning Objective You will transfer a repeating pattern from one representation to another.

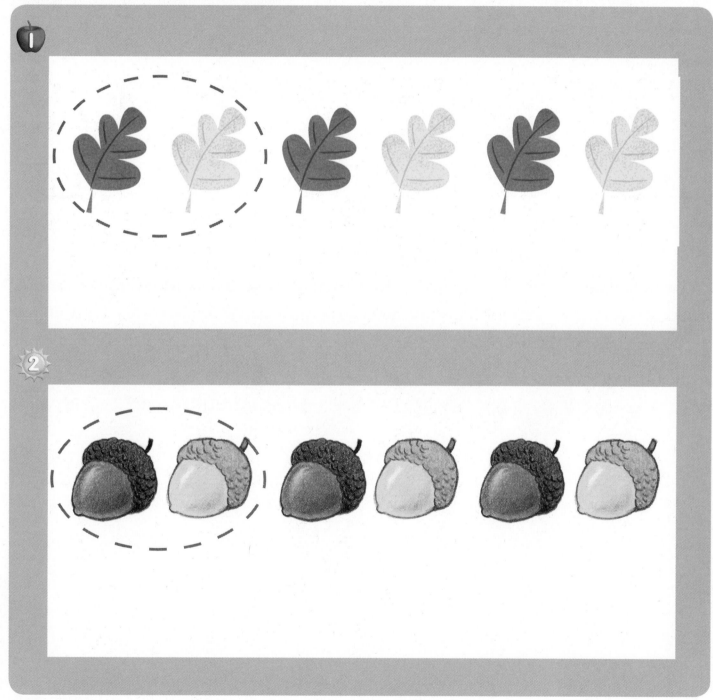

DIRECTIONS 1–2. Look at the pattern. Trace the circle to show the core of the pattern. Use counters to show the same pattern. Draw the pattern.

Virginia SOL Success • 12.5d

one hundred three 103

3 ✓

4 ✓

DIRECTIONS **3–4.** Look at the pattern. Circle to show the core of the pattern. Use counters to show the same pattern. Draw the pattern.

5

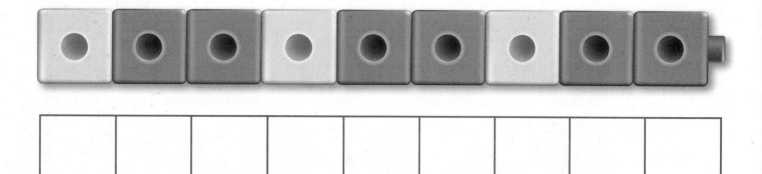

6

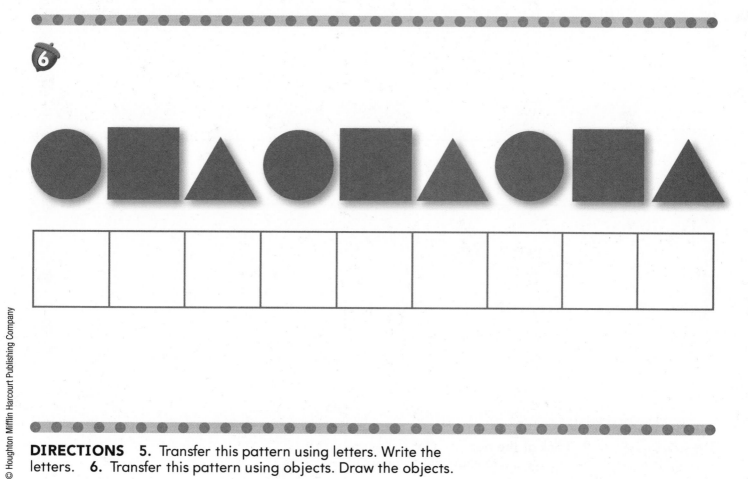

DIRECTIONS **5.** Transfer this pattern using letters. Write the letters. **6.** Transfer this pattern using objects. Draw the objects.

© Houghton Mifflin Harcourt Publishing Company

Problem Solving • Applications Real World

7

WRITE Math

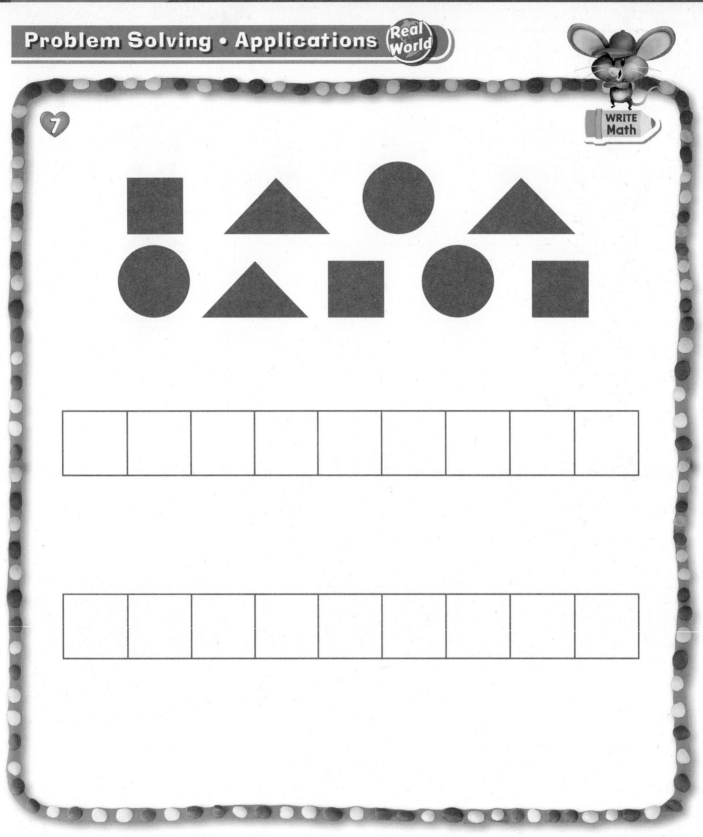

DIRECTIONS 7. Use the shapes shown above to create a repeating pattern in the top grid. Transfer this pattern using objects. Draw the objects in the bottom grid.

Name _____

Algebra • Transfer a Pattern

Learning Objective You will transfer a repeating pattern from one representation to another.

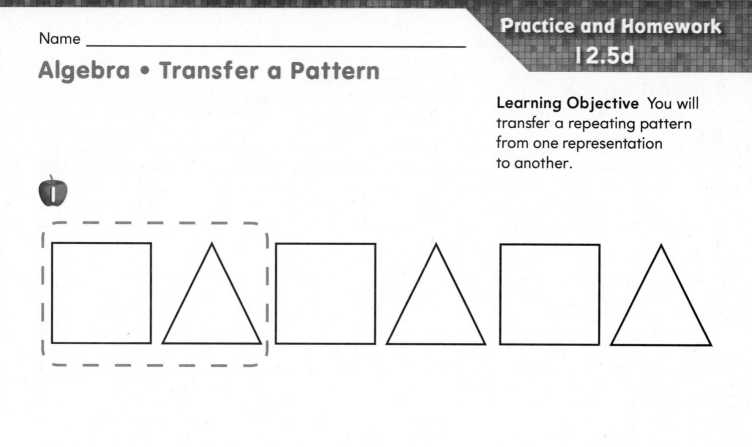

DIRECTIONS **1.** Look at the pattern. Trace the circle to show the core of the pattern. Use counters to show the same pattern. Draw the pattern. **2.** Look at the pattern. Circle to show the core of the pattern. Use counters to show the same pattern. Draw the pattern.

Virginia SOL Success • 12.5d

Lesson Check

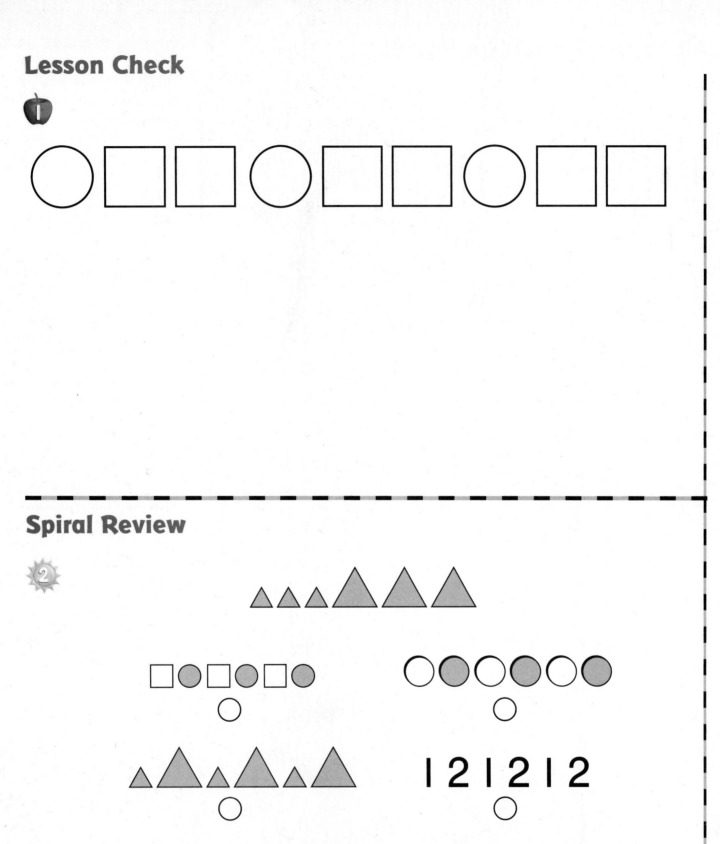

Spiral Review

DIRECTIONS 1. Look at the pattern. Circle to show the core of the pattern. Use counters to show the same pattern. Draw the pattern. 2. Which pattern could you create from these counters? Mark under your answer.

108 one hundred eight